Praise for *The EduProtocol Field Guide Math Edition*

No matter the age of the students you teach, Math EduProtocols should be your go-to tool. They are easy to implement, minimize teacher prep time, and help students focus on truly understanding why and how math works.

—**Nancy Minicozzi,** M.Ed., instructional coach

The thoughtful guidelines, tips and multiple grade-level connections for each Eduprotocol bear witness to the experiences of two veteran educators and a passion to take learning to new levels.

—**Scott Ellingson,** math educator/principal

Lisa and Jeremiah bring their experience coaching teachers at a perfect time in education, as educators seek methods of increasing student motivation with deep learning experiences that can be applied to a physical, hybrid, or distance environment. A must-have for mathematics teachers and coaches that will be referenced again and again.

—**Katherine Goyette,** educational technology and integrated studies consultant, Tulare County Office of Education

Jeremiah and Lisa have brought back a way for teachers to boost that confidence and mastery in the math classroom by allowing students time for practice, feedback, and repetition of concepts. The activities presented in this book allow teachers a low-prep way to build math fluency and number sense without worksheets and timed math tests.

—**Meghan Johann,** teacher

EduProtocols are solid as skill-building strategies, and fun to learn and teach. At the same time, they are flexible and adaptable for framing all kinds of content areas and levels! I especially love how the protocols honor student voice and agency over their own learning by using tech tools in ways that promote mastery, creativity, and engagement. Plus the tech tools make them super adaptable to remote learning.

—**Angela Der Ramos,** fifth-grade teacher, Bardin Elementary, Salinas, CA

This book provides a practical blueprint for teachers of all levels to incorporate fun, interactive, and collaborative EduProtocols for math learning and retention! I highly recommend it for any mathematics teacher looking to increase student understanding for their diverse learners.

—**Shane Ferguson,** assistant principal, Milford High School

The protocols seamlessly promote equitable practices and support Universal Design for Learning as well as the development of executive functions inside the mathematics classroom. This book is sure to become a go-to resource for educators across all disciplines!

—**Melynee Naegele,** K-8 mathematics specialist, Claremore Public Schools

I can't recommend this book enough! If you are looking for a high-energy, confidence-building, fun, and fulfilling way to practice the most important math skills every day, you can't go wrong.

—**Jenna Rodgers,** MS.Ed, second-grade teacher

The EduProtocol Field Guide Math Edition

The EduProtocol
FIELD GUIDE
MATH EDITION

— 15 —

Student-Centered Lesson
Frames for Math Mastery

Lisa Nowakowski & Jeremiah Ruesch

Forewords by Marlena Hebern & Jon Corippo

The EduProtocol Field Guide Math Edition: 15 Student-Centered Lesson Frames for Math Mastery

This book is available at special discounts when purchased in quantity for educational purposes or for use as premiums, promotions, or fundraisers. For inquiries and details, contact the publisher at books@daveburgessconsulting.com.

Published by Dave Burgess Consulting, Inc.
San Diego, CA
DaveBurgessConsulting.com

Library of Congress Control Number: 2021930995
Paperback ISBN: 978-1-951600-74-7
Ebook ISBN: 978-1-951600-75-4

Cover and interior design by Liz Schreiter
Editing and book production by Reading List Editorial: readinglisteditorial.com

Jeremiah

I'd like to dedicate this book to my son, Malakiah, for inspiring me to be better, and my wife, Elizabeth, for making me better.

Lisa

I'd like to dedicate this book to my father, Gary, and Grandpa Zig for instilling a love of learning, especially when it comes to math.

Contents

Math and I have a strange relationship. All the way through school, it was the mysterious subject to me. I did the work, poorly, and got Cs in math basically all the way through school. I barely escaped my last college math class with a 70.6 percent—in a pass/fail class no less. I ended my "career in math" in the same blur that I had started it in. In fact, I chose my major—advertising—because there were no additional math classes required.

Then an odd thing happened. At work, I started working with a lot of databases in FileMaker Pro on my Mac Classic. That led to making a lot of charts. I was analyzing data and doing logical functions in FileMaker every day at work. Suddenly, math was useful. Not only that, but math was actually cool. I loved my spreadsheets and FileMaker work. On my first ever attempt at a big bid, over $1 million, I was over by only $2,000 . . . and I was competing with a firm that had bidders who'd been doing the work for a decade.

Then another thing happened: I switched careers. My wife talked me into education. I was so excited as I began visiting and student teaching in classes. As I entered my first classroom that was to be my own, my blood ran cold—*I have to teach math*. Uh-oh. I had forgotten about that part.

Since I had poor math skills, this was going to be a challenge. I had a couple of things working in my favor, though. First was empathy: I was going to be learning with the kids, not just teaching them. Second, I wasn't overly indoctrinated into any particular "camp," thanks to my deft avoidance of pre-service training in this area. I was a blank slate, ready to explore the opportunities as they emerged. And third: I was game. I flat-out loved teaching, and would have figured out a way to teach the phone book if told to. Unsurprisingly, my math skills quickly grew. I realized that math itself was not the problem I had with math. It was the pedagogy of lecture/ worksheets combined with delayed feedback that was the problem.

In fact, the very first EduProtocol that Marlena and I created together was inspired by my aversion to math. It was based on a Frayer model–looking graphic organizer and was an instant hit with teachers and students. Little did anyone know that this EduProtocol was the result of over a decade of observing what *did not work* in my classrooms with students and math.

This book is designed to accomplish two main ideas: helping *all students* achieve math mastery while at the same time *reducing* teacher workloads. When all students can learn the content, we don't just maximize their future economic opportunities—just as importantly, we acknowledge that we can all be "math people." And in case you haven't noticed, parents, students, and educational institutions all put a great value on "math people." But some might ask why reducing teacher workloads is just as important. I would tell them this: When teachers are not overloaded by stacks of paper to correct, feedback is faster, helping students correct course sooner. At the same time, educators can spend more of their valuable hours working on targeted instruction, making math meaningful, and building relationships with students. When those symbiotic conditions are in place, teachers aren't just instructing students anymore. They—you and I—are also feeding their souls.

Foreword
by Marlena Hebern

Everyone in my office knows to fact-check the calendar when they ask me what I am doing on a particular date because I often mix up numbers! That does not mean that I am bad at math—it just means that I am not particularly drawn to numbers. When Common Core arrived around 2009, I was a district ELA coach. We were all struggling to understand the changes in instruction that were coming our way, and I was asked to attend a math standards unpacking conference. Before I knew it, I was sitting in a room of high school math teachers and administrators. I awkwardly looked around, digesting my situation and silently pledging to play it cool.

The workshop was about looking for patterns in equations. We were presented with an algebra problem to solve using manipulatives, but we were also told to find equations in the patterns. I somehow lucked out and discovered the pattern before the other middle and high school teachers, and so, consistent with the Common Core standards, I was asked to share my solution and thinking in front of the whole group. I barely had an explanation for solving the problem, as my solution stemmed from a visualization of the patterns rather than the equations. But I went to the board and tried my best anyway. Immediately, from the back of the room, a tall, intimidating man loudly critiqued my explanation, saying that the rows of my solution were not lined up properly and that as a teacher of math I should know better.

Of course I know that straight rows are important when teaching math, but I was sharing my solution as a learner and not as a teacher. If it were not for the fact that I was writing on a waist-level 24-by-30-inch pad of paper with a Sharpie, I would have erased my work, fixed it, and ducked back into my seat with my head down. But instead I muddled through. As the facilitator moved onto the next problem, all I could hear myself thinking was, "Hey! I solved this problem without understanding all of the math! I made sense of it! I am not a confident math learner, but I did it!"

I learned something really important that day: Being a learner isn't easy! Not only is it hard work, but being vulnerable is even harder. I can trace my strengths and weaknesses in math to the year that the concepts were introduced and the teacher I had. In fifth grade, Sister Julie was amazing at teaching fractions, and I got fractions. With decimals and a new teacher the following year, not so much. This uneven teacher skill created gaps in my learning and caused high levels of math anxiety, something that I still struggle with today.

Our role as educators is to grow learners, and growing anything takes time and patience. We try to set up all the right conditions, and then we place the learner into that setting and nudge along the magic until the learner is strong enough to make it on their own. It's like staking tomatoes in a garden: if you offer the right support, suddenly you have these amazingly ripe fruits!

EduProtocols are the stakes in the garden. They help teachers grow confident and adept students. They are part of the gardener's toolkit, and now we have a set of tools specifically designed for the garden of mathematics.

Authors Lisa Nowakowski and Jeremiah Ruesch have not only adapted existing EduProtocols but have created a series of new EduProtocols to support and build confidence and skills in math learners. This book provides so many ways for students to explore math from different perspectives and to honor divergent thinking.

As with any EduProtocols book, the aim is to create a format that, once learned, is comfortable and familiar to teachers and students alike—so comfortable that both can direct their focus to the math itself instead of on the worksheet approach that we so often see as the main diet of learners. While this book is not specifically about defusing math anxiety, we hope that these Math Edu-Protocols will spark magic and create a new reality for learners by creating a supportive environment for learning, exploring, and practicing math.

SECTION 1
Mathematics through the Looking Glass

"Stay" is a charming word in a friend's vocabulary.

—Amos Bronson Alcott, *Concord Days*

Chapter 1
How Lisa and Jeremiah Got Here

Jon

Do you want to do one thing a week for eight weeks or eight things a week for four weeks? Do the math!

Marlena

I remember teaching kindergarten students to measure using unit blocks to measure the length of an object. In first grade, to an inch; in second grade, to the half inch, and on through the grades. By high school, Mr. Hebern (Marlena's woodshop teacher husband) would complain that his students could not measure to the sixteenth inch. Why? They never learned to put it all together!

Our story begins with Lisa sitting in a conference session led by Jon Corippo on the eight parts of speech. Instead of the prototypical "one piece at a time" approach (a focus on nouns for one week, proper nouns the next, then on to plurals, etc.), he introduced all eight parts of speech at once using the 8 p*ARTS EduProtocol. Lisa was intrigued: it made intuitive sense to show students how all the parts *fit together in one place*, and she loved it on sight. Her immediate thought was, "I need something like this for math!" And that's where this book got its start.

Jon and Lisa were on to something. Instead of assuming that the individual parts mattered, they focused on the relationships among the parts. Instead of asking students to work through the individual concepts of each part, their insight was to have students work through all the iterations of the relationships of parts so they see and "feel" the connections from one part to the next.

Lisa wrote about the Place Value MathReps in August 2016. In October, Lisa ran into Jon at the annual fall conference of CUE, our local statewide technology organization. He told Lisa how great he thought the idea was and had her explain it to another educator. Since that time, Jon and Marlena have been MathReps advocates, even putting the MathReps EduProtocol into their first book. You can learn more about MathReps below in section 2: Remixed and Revised EduProtocols.

During one of Jon's sessions at a training event in Jeremiah's district, Jon shared a progression of the 8 p*ARTS EduProtocol that he used in the classroom with his sixth graders. He mentioned that a fifth-grade teacher, Lisa, had adapted the 8 p*ARTS EduProtocol to math. Armed with this new information, Jeremiah sought out Lisa to see what she had created, as he wanted to try it with his own students. Lisa had designed several examples for different elementary grade levels, so Jeremiah asked a few teachers in his district if they would let him try her MathReps in their classes, and they were happy to let him experiment. As Jon and Marlena explain in chapter 3, although students were confused at first, by the end of the session they were able to fluidly navigate the MathReps materials and begin mastering the content.

Jeremiah's initial success with MathReps opened the doors for him to see new possibilities for using EduProtocols. He started thinking about applications for upper grades and got his chance to try them out when one of his district's AP calculus teachers left on maternity leave. The idea of creating MathReps EduProtocols for a calculus class seemed a natural marriage: students needed tools to develop the skills necessary to access the content, which would allow them to explore the conceptual side of calculus during class time. Starting with limits, Jeremiah created a sequence of MathReps that showed all of the multiple ways to represent limits. Students went from not recognizing the various forms of a limit to being able to recognize when limits will fail visually and analytically—all because of the MathReps EduProtocol.

The skill practice of the MathReps extended to differentiation, and integration reinforced the conceptual development students received from their instruction, giving them a tool to make the connection between theory and practice. Later that spring, Lisa found herself sitting in the front row of Jeremiah's Math EduProtocols session at a conference. Soon they got to talking about the value of EduProtocols and shortly thereafter they joined forces to become MathReps EduProtocol champions.

The following year Jeremiah and Lisa were approached by Jon and Marlena with the idea of writing an EduProtocols book

Jeremiah

Once students master the conceptual understanding, they need more practice moving through the connected skills and iterations: for example, fraction bars to fractions to decimals and back again with fluidity.

Jon

In Jeremiah's class, kids completed his MathReps in five minutes—the result of conceptual understanding and practice.

Our Professional Learning Networks can bring us together in unexpected ways to make us better educators. Reach out to us at @nowatechie, @mathkaveli, @mhebern, @jcorippo, and #EduProtocols and #MathReps! We'd love to connect with you!

---

focused on math. "Um, yes, please!" They had both been using MathReps and adapting existing EduProtocols to fit the needs of their students. The timing was perfect, as both Jeremiah and Lisa were going to be at the same conference later that same month. There they were able to sit down and discuss their ideas. The conversation covered the gamut of their experiences and settled on the central idea of a systematic way to provide mathematical access for kids. It was also important to both that all the Common Core Mathematical Practices were well represented throughout. Lisa and Jeremiah began exploring and expanding on what they had been using in order to assemble a variety of Math EduProtocols.

When they first began adapting EduProtocols in math, they found several they were comfortable with, such as Frayer Model (chapter 8) or Iron Chef (which they adapted to become Sous Chef, chapter 9). In each of these, Lisa and Jeremiah saw the potential to connect, or bridge, ideas and concepts. Each of these could easily be adapted to allow students to see and practice the different methods of a concept, such as adding fractions. Having students represent a problem using the area model, number line, tape diagram, and algorithm all at once allowed them to naturally make the connections between them and the *why* of how it all works. Jeremiah and Lisa were after the deeper understanding.

Creating new Math EduProtocols allowed the authors to explore their creative sides. Many of the new ones were inspired by proven pedagogy: Write Bytes (chapter 17) was inspired by Number Talks, short number exercises to help students develop number fluency. In Number Talks, students explore how to break down a problem, or image into understandable parts. For example, to calculate 45 + 87, a student would break it down to add 40 + 80 and then add 5 + 7. With Number Talks, there can be more than one way to break down the problem, and students, as a group, explore the different options.

This allows students to see problems through various lenses. In Write Bytes, the same concept is applied with a twist. Comic Strip Math (chapter 16) was inspired by a group of students obsessed with comic books. Convince Me That (chapter 19) focuses on a student's ability to communicate understanding rather than solve a problem simply in order to obtain an answer.

After many conversations, and a lot of hard work, the vision transformed into a reality they call Math EduProtocols. Now, they are ready to release these amazing mind-set shifts to teachers worldwide!

In this book, you will find seven of the original EduProtocols adapted beautifully for math and eight brand-new EduProtocols created just for math that span the grades from kindergarten through high school! Enjoy!

Chapter 2
Cyber Sandwich

"It's magic," the chief cook concluded, in awe. "No, not magic," the ship's doctor replied. "It's much more. It's mathematics."

—David Brin, *Glory Season*

What are Math EduProtocols? Math EduProtocols are lesson frames that can be used with a wide variety of math curriculums. They are designed to allow students to engage in discussions, practice thinking with agility, and develop creativity as they show what they know. Math EduProtocols are tools for teachers to use in their curriculum to teach skills and the process of thinking and analysis.

Before delving further into the philosophy on which EduProtocols are built, we think it's a good idea to show an EduProtocol in action. Seeing is believing, and we think it's important to provide a baseline to refer to as we explore how EduProtocols function in the classroom. The Cyber Sandwich EduProtocol is a useful one to present, as it has appeared in both *EduProtocol Field Guides*—but not in a mathematical context. If you are already familiar with Cyber Sandwich, this section will serve to refresh yourself with its elements, remixed and reformulated for mathematics. And don't worry—we have plenty of new protocols later in the book!

As you read through this first math protocol, think about its core features. How is an EduProtocol different from a worksheet? How might an EduProtocol help students learn how to think creatively and with agility? How might students work with their peers to deepen their understanding of the material presented? And, most importantly, how does an EduProtocol make learning fun?

This Cyber Sandwich EduProtocol features paired collaboration: students compare their understanding of the topic with a partner without simply copying the work of their partner. This simple yet powerful structure provides support for students and English language learners through a rhythm of working alone, then working together, and finally working alone again as they construct their final understanding of the content. Use this protocol to examine and deconstruct word problems and conceptual math content.

Academic Goals:

- Students collaboratively compare and contrast their understanding of a single topic.
- Students develop their own understanding of the topic.
- Students are held accountable through producing proof of comprehension.

Math Practices:

- CCSS MATH PRACTICE: MP1: Make sense of problems and persevere in solving them.
- CCSS MATH PRACTICE: MP7: Look for and make use of structure.

Teacher Big Ideas:

- Students use scaffolded support from a partner to develop a deeper understanding of the problem or content.
- Language learners are provided an opportunity to talk through the process prior to crafting answers.

Description:

Guided exploration is a compelling tool for learners, and Cyber Sandwich is a powerfully engaging and straightforward EduProtocol that allows students to be learners in their own right. Students first review the problem independently to develop their own understanding and strategies, then work with a partner to compare and contrast their findings, and end by independently summarizing their joint findings using the notes of both partners.

Prepare for the Activity:

To get started, use the digital template at eduprotocols.com/cyber-sandwich-template or create your own similar to the one below. Consider how you will pair students up, including sitting locations and space for discussions. Be clear about what you want the students to comprehend, and find a word problem for students to

Marlena

This is a comprehension protocol. Give students a moment to stop and think about the content before moving on.

Lisa

Allowing students to think before collaborating gives them the processing time needed to fully understand the task. Collaborating with a partner and reflecting are crucial skills in today's world. You are teaching your students lifelong skills that will serve them well beyond the EduProtocol.

consider. Craft prompts or sentence stems to help direct students in their discussions, for example:

- *What is the problem asking you to do?*
- *What are the key numbers you will need to use to get your answer?*
- *What calculations will you need to make?*

Instructions:

Step 1: Launch the task by giving students five to ten minutes to read through the word problem on their own. They should highlight words that are keywords and make notes on what the problem is asking them to do. Students may complete the first step of setting up the problem but should not solve the problem.

Step 2: Partner students up and give them an additional five to ten minutes to move their notes and problem set-up to the Venn diagram. After students complete the Venn diagram, ask them to discuss the similarities and differences in each partner's notes.

Step 3: Instruct students to write independently about what they discussed with their partner and how the problem will be solved. Students may also solve the problem in this step if so desired (if students are recording their notes in an electronic template, using paper is okay for solving the problem). Students reflect and write a summary, use voice-capturing software, or create a video of what they now know.

Key Points to Remember:

- Start with a non-academic or previously mastered concept (to lower the academic cognitive load as students learn the process of the protocol).
- New is messy, but proficiency will build over time.
- Once the technology and the protocol are mastered, apply the EduProtocol to more difficult conceptual problems.

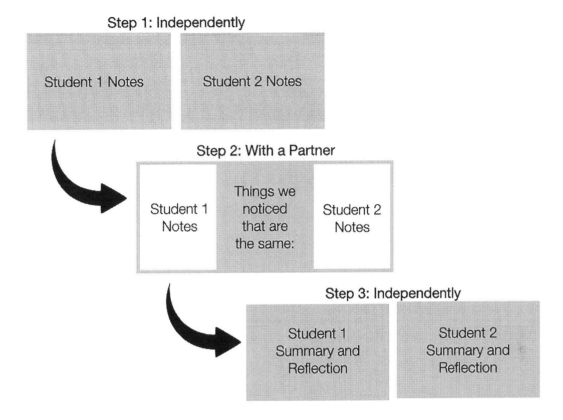

Adaptations for Primary Students:

Consider introducing this protocol on paper prior to using technology, but also consider the unique ability of slides to house digital manipulatives that students can use. If staying in the digital realm, use content that is embedded in the slides. If recording student conversations is important, consider using voice-capturing software or video-capturing software such as Flipgrid. And remember to always start with very easy content until students understand what they are doing at each step of this protocol.

Pro Tip:

Once you use Cyber Sandwich for understanding word problems, you will see the potential for implementing this powerful comprehension protocol with other aspects of your math curriculum. Consider using your math text as well as online math videos for content.

Reflect on Your Experience:

Try this math protocol with your students a few times and observe how it works. Consider the experience of your students. How did you see them responding? Were they approaching the math question in creative new ways? Did you notice them having agile and insightful discussions? Did they emerge with a deeper understanding of the problem-solving process? Students are performing many skills all at once. Repetition builds skill, and EduProtocols are designed to be used over and over with changing content. If you didn't see students achieving these goals right away, keep repeating the protocol to ensure students are developing the skills needed to use this new way of interacting effectively.

Fluency with Learning Tools:

What makes Cyber Sandwich a protocol? The math content can change easily enough, but now students will know exactly what to do when you say, "We're doing a Cyber Sandwich today!" Students of any age will know they're going to pair off, start analyzing a math problem, come together to discuss their notes and put them into a Venn diagram, then break off to write their answers. It is a flow they will be familiar with because you taught it to them, and now you can pull out this protocol in just a moment's notice and everyone will know what to expect.

But the benefits of EduProtocols don't end there. Now you are free to roam the classroom, ask and answer questions about the problem, respond to individual students, and help with analyzing the problem. These protocols are a classroom game-changer because they allow the teacher to provide personal feedback in real time. Students will not be raising their hand to ask, "Teacher, what do I do now?" because they will already know what to do. Instead, they'll be asking questions about their conceptual understanding of the content—exactly what you want to hear. Cyber Sandwich works with any kind of problem that requires thinking and showing your work.

What content do you teach that might be suitable for you to use with the Cyber Sandwich EduProtocol?

Chapter 3
What Are EduProtocols?

*Strong teachers don't teach content; Google has content.
Great teachers focus on connections and relationships.*

—Greg Reynolds

Before diving deeper into the new Math EduProtocols, it will be helpful to explore the concept of EduProtocols as delivery vessels for content and how and why they work as tools for student engagement and learning.

EduProtocols are dynamic and versatile lesson frames that are used to deliver content across grade levels. Each lesson frame is designed to be used over and over with changing content. While some EduProtocols, like MathReps, are specific to standards at a particular grade level, most protocols, like Cyber Sandwich, are suitable for any grade level and can be used throughout the year as curriculum progresses. EduProtocols can be adapted to fit the needs of a particular classroom, learning situation, topic of study, or student in need, and they can be used to support a Universal Design for Learning (UDL) environment. EduProtocols are gamified or structured in a way that students find enjoyable, and in varying degrees include one or more of the Four Cs.

The Four Cs, identified by the Partnership for 21st Century Skills, are four skills considered essential for modern students, skills that successful adults use every day:

Collaboration: Using interpersonal and intrapersonal skills when working with peers.

Communication: Sharing one's work, research, and projects with other students and adults inside and outside the four walls of the classroom.

Critical Thinking: Analyzing problems, data, research, literature, or mathematics by solving real-world problems.

Creativity: Open-ended and choice-driven activities in which *students* have autonomy in the process and results so creativity can flourish.

It takes most classes two to five repetitions of an EduProtocol to master it. The sweet spot is achieved when automaticity is reached and the student's focus shifts from how to complete the process to mastering the content. To help you wrap your brain around this concept, think of EduProtocols through the lens of posting an image on Instagram.

Posting to Instagram or any social media can be challenging the very first time. But it gets easier with practice.

There are several steps to posting an image:

- Find the perfect shot
- Snap the image
- Open the app
- Add the image to the app
- Adjust the color and other edit options
- Write and tag your post with hashtags
- Wait for your friends to see your picture and comment

Next time you find that perfect shot, you will repeat the same basic steps to post the image. The steps remain the same, but the image and the circumstances for taking the perfect shot change each time you post.

It feels complicated at first. You might struggle to find just the right edits, perhaps. However, with a little practice, the process becomes familiar and you begin to concentrate on the art of framing the perfect composition with the right lighting instead of finding your photo library in the app. When finding someone to follow on Instagram, notice how their photography has evolved from their earliest postings. Students will do the same with EduProtocols: once students grow into the protocols, they will shift their focus from lesson procedures to actual learning.

The Eight-Point PROTOCOL Checklist below explores the elements that make EduProtocols unique and powerful learning tools for any face-to-face classroom, as well as in digital and blended learning environments.

Eight-Point PROTOCOL Checklist

EduProtocols are structured enough to be consistent from classroom to classroom, yet open-ended enough that students can be creative and have a choice in demonstrating their learning. The lesson design itself is relatively simple and has the ultimate goal of shifting the workload from teacher to student. What makes an EduProtocol? There are eight common characteristics of EduProtocols that make them powerful tools for teaching and learning:

- **EduProtocol = Lesson**—If EduProtocol + EduProtocol + EduProtocol equals a unit, then one EduProtocol is somewhat equal to a lesson. They have substance and are not to be confused with "activities," which we might do within a lesson. These activities—for example, quick write, pair-share, exit tickets, elevator pitches, voting, sentence stems, writing what you learned in the form of a song, or folded-paper books for notes—are not full lessons in themselves.

- **Replicable**—An EduProtocol has a defined structure that can be repeated by other students and teachers. The EduProtocol is named to provide it an identity and to separate it from the content.

- **One to One**—Accountability for each student's part in the activity is a key component of the EduProtocol. The contribution is traceable and provides accountability of participation and evidence of learning.

- **Time Frame**—A fitness trainer wouldn't have a client do bench presses or squats for a full hour. Effective workouts have variety. EduProtocols should be ten to thirty-five minutes in length. Ideally, an EduProtocol does not use the entire class period, thereby allowing students to work on multiple learning events in one period. If you need to, chunk the content so it can be completed in the allotted time.

- **Overtly Connected Standards**—An EduProtocol should feature multiple adopted standards (five to fifteen grade-level standards for math) in a single setting. Kids will struggle on Day 1 but will be rolling by Day 5 as they learn to use multiple skills in a single learning event. (See #1 and #2 under "Best Practices" below for reference.)

- **Cs in Action (Four Cs—Communication, Collaboration, Critical Thinking, and Creativity)**—Do not turn your class into an Edu-gulag with unceasing fill-in-the-blanks-type work. Effective EduProtocols are not just worksheets; they embody open-ended learning and UDL concepts. Whereas worksheets focus on convergence (one correct answer), Edu-Protocols allow for divergent (many and varied) responses. For this reason, if your students don't like a protocol, you are likely doing it incorrectly.

- **Open and Able to Be Used across Multiple Subject Areas**—EduProtocols typically work across multiple subject areas (e.g., an EduProtocol used for science could be used with social studies and language arts) or across multiple standards within a subject (e.g., math-specific EduProtocols could be used to teach the associative property as well as factor trees). There are some protocols that we have designed specifically for math concepts, taking into consideration the unique challenges in the math classroom.

- **Loved by Kids**—Design for children! Take your teacher hat off and tap into your innate creativity. Design something irresistible to students of many ages.

Best Practices

All EduProtocols are designed around these eight factors, but implementing EduProtocols in the SPIRIT they were designed requires something more. Keep SPIRIT in mind while you are sharing the EduProtocols with your students. Below are the six big SPIRIT ideas Jon and Marlena developed for working with kids:

Serious Commitment: We always tell our own children, "If you are going to play a sport or be in a play, commit to the whole season." You can do the same by committing to use the EduProtocol weekly, all semester, or all year long so students gain fluency with the process, which will enable them to focus on the content.

Progression: The EduProtocol begins quickly and easily. The first two reps of an EduProtocol should focus on a non-academic, low-cognitive-load task so students can concentrate on the task and not the content. Educators should simply focus on helping students complete the EduProtocol. Quality may be low at first. Over time you can add skills and subtasks or shorten the time frame to add intensity.

Immediate Feedback: If you are grading an EduProtocol any time other than immediately, your EduProtocol is in danger of losing student intensity. Athletes crave feedback. Chefs come out of the kitchen to see how guests enjoyed the meal. Offer immediate feedback and you'll see a more immediate impact.

Reps: Jon's football coach, Mike Waufle, loved to say, "Reactions are what you do without thinking. The only way to get the very best results is to do a million reps." We can't do a million reps in class, but we can do twenty or thirty to create mastery-level learning.

Interest: Keep the pace just fast enough to hold students' attention by giving them the right amount of content for the right amount of time.

Tech Balance: Please use tools like Quizizz, Kahoot, Google Suite, Flipgrid, and others, but remember that sometimes pa-

Lisa

MathReps fall into the same strand as The Fast and Curious EduProtocol. They are skill-building protocols so that students can spend more time on concept development and application!

Marlena

You'll see a variety of EduProtocols in this book covering a range from skill-building EduProtocols (we sometimes call these Mini or Intro Edu-Protocols) to full-on, open-ended EduProtocols!

Jon

Training and culture-building in the first days of school will make all the difference all year long!

Jeremiah

This is true in face-to-face classrooms, blended classrooms, and digital classrooms!

per is faster. Brain research tells us a Frayer or Venn diagram on a sheet of paper can be a super-efficient way to set up for the digital tools that help ideas get synthesized.

EduProtocols should be relatively simple to deploy so you can access them from your grab bag anytime. The PROTOCOL and SPIRIT checklists provide an important framework for the implementation of new EduProtocols in our quest to deepen student engagement, creativity, and outcomes.

Start Slow to Seed Learning

The most successful teachers take time in the first weeks of school to update students on classroom procedures: where to get the paper, when to sharpen pencils, how to put away the laptops, and how to exit the classroom. Experienced teachers understand the importance of training students in the first days of school in face-to-face classrooms.

Yet when it comes to lesson design, be it in the face-to-face classroom, the blended classroom, or the fully online classroom, it is easy to forget that we also need to train students on how to learn! EduProtocols provide a structure to help you set expectations for your class.

A common mistake made when teachers begin to deploy Edu-Protocols in their lessons is to start too fast with too much content. Learning the protocol is hard enough without also having to learn new content at the same time! Teach just the protocol and use light content that students are already familiar with, such as review material or "getting to know you" activities at the beginning of the year. Like any new activity, be it a board game or a sport, the first time playing will be clunky and rough. But once you start to internalize the rules and understand the moves, you quickly become familiar and can enjoy yourself. Once kids get the protocol part down, you can speed up and deliver all kinds of complicated content. Your students will know what to do and how to do it, allowing them—and you—to focus on the content!

Pacing to Increase Opportunity

Unless they're given guidance, most students will use all available time to complete an assignment or task. Some will want even more! An essential aspect of EduProtocols is pacing. Students have little internal sense of time, so moving students along teaches them to finish and to feel good about finishing. With the Math EduProtocols, pacing is key to success. Too fast builds insecurity with math, too slow and students will live in a world of procrastination. The math teacher must find the right balance for their students. For students needing more time than their peers, try front loading the task so slower students can get a head start.

As students work on learning and mastering curriculum, remember to keep them moving forward, both within a protocol and from protocol to protocol. Most of the protocols are designed so one piece of the curriculum is delivered in one period. Later in the book, we will address "stacking" and "smashing" to tackle longer or more complicated pieces of curriculum.

Distributed Practice

EduProtocols work best when using distributed practice rather than massed practice. Cramming for exams in college is an example of massed practice; learning takes place all at once. Distributed practice, on the other hand, which ideally includes breaks of one to two days between reps, allows the brain to synthesize information and grow over time. A whole class deployment schedule for EduProtocols might include practice on Monday, Tuesday, and Thursday, allowing for space on Wednesday to let the brain process information while at rest.

It is for this reason we recommend mixing it up a bit. For example, you may want to rotate weeks with different EduProtocols. Or, do EduProtocols Monday through Thursday and, on Friday, use Comic Strip Math as an assessment. Of course, you will need to teach the Comic Strip Math EduProtocol first, but once they are comfortable with it students will welcome the break, and it will give you a chance to assess a particular standard.

Cycling back to previous EduProtocols for concepts that build upon one another over the year can make an effective spiral review before tackling new concept development.

For example:

- number bonds (part-part-whole) before fact families
- place value before adding double-digit numbers with regrouping
- fractions before decimals

Templates

We have provided several templates on our website, eduprotocols .com, to help you get started. These templates will structure the EduProtocol for students and simplify the deployment process and learning curve. As you and your students become more adept at using EduProtocols, consider minimizing the structure you provide and allowing students a more open and free canvas in which to design. You'll see their creativity shine as they learn to use the space given to them!

Call to Action

New to Protocols?

If EduProtocols are new for you, reread the directions for Cyber Sandwich in the previous chapter and then use Cyber Sandwich with students this week. Be sure to implement this tool several times to give your students the benefits of repetition.

Seasoned User

If you are familiar with EduProtocols generally and/or Cyber Sandwich in particular, consider what content you're about to teach that would be successfully tackled through the protocol. Try and imagine the learning outcome you're aiming for and whether Cyber Sandwich is the best EduProtocol to help you get your students to that point.

Give a man a fish and you feed him for a day. Teach him how to fish and you feed him for a lifetime.

—Chinese Proverb

We asked Dr. Sonny Magana to write a guest chapter for this math edition of EduProtocols because Dr. Magana's research on the T3 Framework supports the EduProtocols. In the chapter below, Sonny explains how the T3 Framework and the EduProtocols go together like peanut butter and jelly. The T3 Framework is the why and the EduProtocols is the how. Together, students can engage in deeper learning and increased retention using structured lesson frames.

Learning How to Learn by Dr. Sonny Magana

It is exciting to see EduProtocols grow into math with Lisa and Jeremiah. I first met Marlena Hebern and Jon Corippo at a conference soon after the publication of their first book, *The EduProtocols Field Guide.* I had just released my second book, *Disruptive Classroom Technologies,* in which I synthesized nearly forty years of research on innovative EdTech into what I called the T3 Framework for Innovation. Marlena, Jon, and I immediately fell into a groove and were excited to discover that our perspectives were so harmonious. We exchanged books. I attended their conference sessions on EduProtocols, and they attended my sessions on implementing the T3 Framework learning strategies.

We quickly saw how EduProtocols lesson frames complemented the T3 strategies, making them more actionable and easier to implement, while the T3 Framework provided a specific sequence of learning that was shown to quadruple learning performance. We decided then and there to combine our respective bodies of work aligning EduProtocols to the research-driven strategies in the T3 Framework. Our goal for this book is not just to help students learn math, but to help students learn *how* to learn math so they can embrace mathematical learning for a lifetime.

Since many of you reading this book are familiar with EduProtocols, this chapter will tell the story of the T3 Framework and how this next-generation model of pedagogy was built from the learning habits I acquired during my experience of learning how to learn music. Like any good story, mine begins with an essential question: what do rock and roll, educational technology, and limitless student learning have in common?

I Love Rock and Roll

In 1964, I first heard the genre of music that would indelibly change my life. My mom had a black plastic transistor radio she would listen to after putting me and my siblings down for our afternoon naps. A hyper-curious toddler, I remember noticing a strange noise that demanded further exploration. The sweet sound of Petula Clark singing "Downtown" met me like a familiar friend. I remember thinking to myself, "It's like sugar for my ears!" I didn't understand it, but I knew I wanted more. A few months later, the Beatles made their debut on *The Ed Sullivan Show* and introduced a new generation of Americans to rock and roll. That performance sealed the deal for me: The songs. The guitars. The haircuts. I was hooked. The Beatles became the soundtrack to my formative years.

In school I was a compliant, if uninspired, student. I learned to love stories from an early age, so while I was proficient in my studies, I didn't really love learning in school. I was far more passionate about the Beatles than I was about schoolwork. I pored over every book, article, and fan magazine I could get my hands on. Then, in 1970, disaster struck. The Beatles broke up.

The Commitments

The breakup didn't stop the Liverpool lads from composing, arguably, some of their greatest music. John Lennon's song "Imagine," an instant classic, was released in the fall of 1971. Suddenly, I was compelled to learn how to play that song.

My dad had a dusty old Sears and Roebuck guitar, a relic from his youth. Sadly, he never learned to play it. It was a 1950s Silvertone model with a sunburst finish and nylon strings. Sometimes I would pick up my dad's guitar and, though it wasn't in tune and I had no idea what I was doing, I would pretend to play and sing along with Beatles records. It seemed so monumentally difficult to actually learn how to play that I just faked it. Simply pretending left me feeling strangely hollow and unsatisfied—but how could I learn something that was so out of my reach?

The desire to learn how to play "Imagine" overtook me, and so I decided to stop pretending and committed to *learn* how to play that song on the guitar. I made my first commitment to mastery. It's funny, but I actually *imagined* myself learning how to play "Imagine." That was really all it took. I purchased a cheap guitar songbook from a local music store and set about learning how to tune my father's guitar and play that song.

This kind of experiential learning was vastly different from the rote learning that I experienced in school—particularly in math class where I would follow rote formulas without really understanding what I was doing. My teachers would tell me what to memorize and, being dutiful, I would aspire to attain the goals they set for me. I was merely complying with the wishes of someone other than myself. But when it came to learning how to play the guitar, I was the one who had established the objective. It was all mine. I had clear criteria to determine my level of progress, a set of strategies, and a full personal commitment to achieve my objective. *I made a habit of committing myself to my own mastery goals.*

The very first learning habit math students need to develop is establishing their personal mastery goals and committing to them by writing them down. This is not to stay that students should simply copy the grade-level standards given to their teachers; standards are written in language for adults, not kids. What I am suggesting is teachers must make learning intention and success criteria for every math lesson so clear and understandable to students that they can rewrite them in their own words with clarity and accuracy. This may seem like a superficial exercise, but it most certainly is not. Without the clear guidance provided by personal mastery goals that they commit to, students are adrift in a sea of math concepts like a ship without a rudder.

Plays Well with Others

I carried my guitar with me everywhere I went. I played it on my neighbor's back stoop. I played it on the curb in front of my house. I played it up in a tree. I was getting better by myself, but eventually I wanted to play with others as well.

One day I brought my guitar to school and instantly connected with other budding guitarists. It turned out that we were all learning to play the same songs. Rock and roll was our common language. The nerds, jocks, loners, National Honor Society scholars—it didn't matter. We all taught one another new chords, songs, and styles of playing. Learning from and teaching one another was a newfound joy. More importantly, we talked about learning how to play music all the time.

Until then, I had never experienced a learning situation in which everyone wanted to contribute to the learning of everyone else. This was different from the type of interactions I had had in school. In most of my classroom experiences, the learning was competitive, repetitive, and boring. Talking was strictly prohibited. Listening and furiously copying down and trying to memorize every word my teachers said was what I thought learning was all about. Most of my classrooms felt far more like competition than contribution, with equal amounts of envy for the students who excelled as disdain for students who struggled. None of those dynamics seemed to apply when it came to learning how to play rock and roll.

Learning to play music wasn't effortless, but it was a lot of fun. It also didn't jive with my conception of school learning. Every single person I met wanted to help me become a better guitarist. It was quite natural for me to reciprocate and help others who weren't quite as advanced. I found that I was a patient teacher and discovered, to my utter shock, that teaching someone what I knew improved my own playing significantly. My guitar pals and I were part of a larger collective, all invested in one another's musical mastery and well-being. Unlike in the classroom, I was learning more content and mastering new skills better and faster—because of the group. I made a habit of becoming a valued member of a contributive learning group.

The next habit math students need to develop is talking about their growing understanding of math concepts with their class-mates. Humans are social creatures and so we tend make sense of new and confounding information by talking about it—even the mistakes we make. Every EduProtocol in this book can be used as a prompt for students to talk about what they are doing, what they are learning, and, perhaps more importantly, what they are thinking. Getting students to develop the habit of making their learning visible is really important, but getting students into the habit of making their *thinking* about their learning visible is even more important.

The Van Halen Framework

One sun-drenched afternoon, I was riding in the passenger seat of my friend's car when he popped a cassette into the 8-track player of his souped-up 1978 Chevy Nova—with obscenely large speak-ers propped up in the rear window well. The next ninety seconds changed my life forever. The 8-track was Van Halen's first studio album, and the track was a song called "Eruption."

It was like a swift kick to the head. I'd never heard anything like that. I had no idea that those kinds of sounds could be pro-duced by a single electric guitar. The wizard behind all of it? The legendary Eddie Van Halen.

Eddie's masterful fretwork was rendered on a guitar that he built specifically to produce a tone unlike any other guitar that had previously existed. It was mesmerizing. "Eruption" took me completely out of my comfort zone. I knew I couldn't go back to just playing the same old songs over and over again. I had to learn more.

Listening to a local rock radio station a short time later, none other than Eddie Van Halen was the special guest on a popular morning show. The DJ asked Eddie a question that is forever burned on my brain: "Eddie, do you have any advice for budding guitar players here in the Delaware Valley?" Eddie paused for a moment. Then he said, "Yes, I do. You're probably playing songs on the guitar that you know from the radio, or maybe you bought a book and learned to play songs with open chords and are singing along. That's how you start; that's how I started. But . . ." He paused for a dramatic moment. "If you want to get better, you have to know that you're in a stage. It's a stage that I call the 'Campfire Stage,' because you're probably sitting around a campfire strumming your guitar, playing songs that you learned from the radio, making friends and meeting girls, and that's great." I felt as though Eddie were talking directly to me; I held my breath as he continued.

"Every guitarist," Eddie went on, "has gone through the Campfire Stage, but in order to be a great guitarist you have to go through another stage that I call the 'Chuck Berry Stage.' Every great guitarist has gone through the Chuck Berry Stage of guitar playing. You've got to learn how to rock like Chuck. You've got to learn how to play all those riffs and licks like the back of your hand." John DeBella chimed in then, saying, "Okay, so there's a Campfire Stage, and a Chuck Berry Stage. Is there another stage?" Eddie was almost reverential when he said, "The next stage is the most important stage, and the hardest to get to. That's when you invent an entirely new style of playing that is all your own. Once you get to that stage, you are all by yourself, and it's amazing. But you've got to really want it. You've got to work hard to get there. You can't fake it."

Three stages of learning guitar: Campfire, Chuck Berry, and Eddie Van Halen. I clearly knew that I was in the first stage. I also clearly knew that if I wanted to get better, I would have to start learning how to rock on the guitar like Chuck Berry. That was my next stage. I immediately bought my first Chuck Berry record and set about learning how to play his greatest hits. Thanks to Eddie Van Halen, learning how to play "Rock and Roll Music," "Roll Over Beethoven," and, of course, "Johnny B. Goode" consumed me.

That interview forever altered my view of learning. In just a few minutes, Eddie Van Halen gave me a conceptual framework that, to this day, helps me think about learning to learn music. His guitar-playing framework was a lens that provided a meaningful context to my learning journey. It also gave me milestones from which I could determine how close I was to achieving my goals. I could readily see that I was in the initial stage of learning, the Campfire Stage. I wanted to get better, so I knew that I had to invest the time and energy to learn how to play like Chuck Berry before I could attain the highest stage, in which I was inventing a new style of music that was all my own. I made a habit of using conceptual frameworks to provide context and meaningful feedback for my learning journey.

The third habit math students need to develop is to create their own feedback loops to monitor and track their emotions, effort, and progress toward their mastery goals. While it's important for teachers to monitor and track student progress, it's even more important for students to learn how to do this themselves. What's more, students that take the time to engage in this type of self-reflection gain greater self-awareness and, over time, greater self-determination. I don't think this can be taught; it has to be learned by experience. This habit helps students develop self-regulation strategies, expand upon the learning strategies they use, and build a personal sense of agency or efficacy.

These three new learning habits, from my book *The Seven Habits of Meta Learners*, didn't just help me learn how to play the guitar. They helped me learn how to learn. It seemed odd that this was something I experienced outside of rather than in school. Learning in school was a tiresome and tedious process. My classroom learning habits were equally rote, informed by playing the "Pump and Dump" game: I would pump as many facts as I could into my working memory and then dump them into some examination—ideally before I had forgotten what I memorized. My classroom learning strategies were not aimed at acquiring and consolidating deep conceptual understanding, or for making my knowledge useful by transferring what I knew into different learning contexts. I was dispassionately exercising and developing my working and short-term memory systems only to acquire and briefly retain superficial knowledge.

In contrast, early in my musical journey I realized that learning how to learn could be a natural and joyful process. I was passionate about learning, practicing, and performing music. I didn't just learn how to play the music; I learned how to optimize my learning. I was keenly aware that I employed certain strategies so often that they became habits. I began refining and applying these habits into other pursuits and discovered that there was an immediate and positive impact regardless of the content I was learning. Learning how I learned best became my go-to approach to learning anything and everything.

I would commit myself to new learning in such a way that I would be able to teach the new content better than it had been taught to me. I raised my own learning bar from simple proficiency, or even competency, to mastery. I felt compelled to share my learning habits with others, and so at the age of twenty-three I made the commitment to become a teacher.

The T3 Framework

I have been a teacher since 1983. As fate would have it I also began my career as a researcher that same year, investigating the impact of educational technologies on student engagement and learning. Since then, I have published numerous research studies, journal articles, and books on disruptive innovation in education with the singular focus of helping students leverage educational technologies to develop and enhance effective learning habits.

Education research matters immensely—perhaps particularly so in the digital age, because education systems are awash in evidence-free claims and outright fabrications that simple access to technology tools will automatically transform teaching and learning. Access is indeed a critical first step, but too often putting technology tools in the hands of teachers and students is perceived as the final, rather than the first step. In a recent meta-analysis, renowned education researcher John Hattie calculated that the average effect size educational technologies have on student achievement is dismally low and has been that way for decades. The preponderance of research evidence overwhelmingly indicates that we have developed learning systems that are digitally rich yet impact poor.

An effect size is a statical measurement used to determine the impact of a particular practice. Normal growth over one year is 0.4. Any effect size larger than 0.4 has a positive impact on learning.

However, there is cause for renewed optimism. My recent findings strongly suggest that very large gains in student achievement are possible when digital tools are leveraged to enhance learning strategies. I synthesized the findings from my body of research dating back to 1983 into what I call the T3 Framework for Innovation. The T3 Framework is a conceptual model that shows how to more effectively use existing educational technologies to develop students' capacity for learning how to learn. It was directly inspired by Eddie Van Halen's guitar-playing framework. The T3 Framework organizes learning into three hierarchal domains: T1) Translational, T2) Transformational, and T3) Transcendent. Each domain is further organized into elements and strategies that are concrete, observable, and measurable.

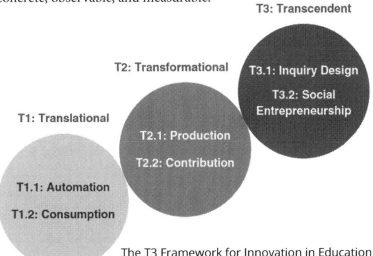

The T3 Framework for Innovation in Education

The T3 Framework and EduProtocols

Modern learning systems can no longer rely on evidence-free opinions to generate meaningful pathways for improving student achievement. Four decades of compounding evidence demonstrates that implementing the strategies in the T3 Framework leads to an extraordinarily large improvement of student learning—specifically, an effect size of 1.6, which is equivalent to quadrupling student learning performance. These research findings were recently vetted, peer-reviewed, and inducted into the Oxford Research Encyclopedia of Education, a global clearinghouse of breakthrough research findings. It is reasonable to suggest that implementing this sequence of strategies in our classrooms will lead to a doubling of student learning performance, perhaps even more.

While the T3 Framework provides clarity and guidance, busy classroom teachers greatly benefit from tools that help them easily implement the T3 strategies. That's where the EduProtocols in this book come into play. EduProtocols serve as cognitive meta-scaffolds that provide the right balance of guidance and divergency to nurture teacher and student creativity while maintaining fidelity to the research-driven T3 strategies. Implementing Edu-Protocols through the lens of the T3 Framework offers a powerful blend of art and science that can be scaled in such a way that every student could realize very large learning gains—not by learning content but by learning how to learn and converting these strategies into lifelong learning habits.

So, what do rock and roll, educational technology, and limitless student learning have in common? Quite a bit, as it turns out. Guiding students to embrace lifelong learning habits will increase the impact of digital technologies on unlocking students' limitless capacities for self-reflection, self-regulation, self-determination, and self-realization.

A reasonable inference can be made that such capacities will better prepare students to address their current learning challenges and the challenges they will encounter in the future. Learning how to optimize how one learns, unlearns, and relearns is *the essential literacy* for the twenty-first century and beyond. Compounding evidence suggests that implementing the research-driven T3 EduProtocols has the capacity to shift educational systems from privileging memorization to celebrating learning how to learn. Nowhere is this concept more important than our classrooms. No time is more essential to begin this work than now. Are you ready to rock and roll?

Call to Action

Sonny progressed though the T3 Framework while learning to play the guitar. Lisa and Jeremiah have also personally progressed through the T3 Framework in their journey into a deeper understanding of EduProtocols. They began with implementing Jon and Marlena's EduProtocols in their classroom (T1: Consumption). Then they began adapting them (T2: Contribution). Finally, they began to create their own (T3: Inquiry Design).

What is your journey? What hobby or skill do you have that has been developed through the T3 Framework? Understanding your own journey can help you understand the journey of your students.

SECTION 2

Remixed and Revised
EduProtocols

*Thousands of candles can be lit from a single candle,
and the life of the candle will not be shortened.
Happiness never decreases by being shared.*

—Gautama Buddha (attributed), *Sutta Nipata*

When we design EduProtocols, we intend to strike an instructional balance: We design lessons that will be used over and over by students to facilitate technology integration into classrooms while inspiring teachers to be the very best instructional leaders they can be. Then we encourage educators to adapt our lesson frames and share them.

This practice of sharing teaching resources is called open pedagogy. We did not make up that term; it has been around for a while and is often used in relationship to open educational resources (OER), which are textbooks that are free and available for teachers and students. Many colleges are promoting open pedagogy in an attempt to reduce the ever-growing cost of textbooks for students, but there are also several excellent OER collections available for K–12 education such as Khan Academy, PowerMyLearning, Big History Project, NROC Project, and Educurious. Many of these sites are funded by foundations in order to provide equitable access to quality educational materials.

OERs are rich learning and teaching materials that are:

- free to access
- free to reuse
- free to revise
- free to remix
- free to redistribute

These five principles of OERs are the foundation of resources used with open pedagogy.

Jon

OERs have the main advantage of being produced by folks with passion and vision. Many corporate-designed products lack that soul.

EduProtocols as Open Pedagogy

We call EduProtocols open pedagogy because while EduProtocols are copyrighted material and should not be published elsewhere without our permission, we *do* encourage you to use them freely in your classrooms and to reuse, revise, remix, and share with your colleagues in person and on social media. Take time to get to know them. Understand the principles underlying EduProtocols and try some protocols in the classroom. Learn the structures of the protocol you want to use, and when you're ready, find natural ways to adapt and modify it to meet the learning needs of your students. Don't be afraid to try someone else's methods. Kids are kids, so what works with one class will probably work with another! You can join the EduProtocol community on Twitter and share what you've used with the hashtag #EduProtocols so others can use, share, and remix your work! Many of the best EduProtocol ideas have come from remixing the work of others.

Giving Credit to the Work of Others

Use the Creative Commons Attribution-ShareAlike citation when remixing and sharing EduProtocols that were created by someone else. You may use, remix, tweak, and build upon them as you wish, but make sure you give credit to the creator and allow new users the same freedom to adapt your work as well.

Naming EduProtocols

Give significantly redesigned EduProtocols a new identity by renaming them. Doing so keeps students from getting confused about the processes involved in a given protocol. If, for instance, the Cyber Sandwich has been significantly redesigned but retains its name, students may not realize they are embarking on a different learning activity when you announce, "Next up is a Cyber Sandwich." They will most likely transfer knowledge from a prior session of that EduProtocol to this one. EduProtocols are intended to reduce student stress and affective filters, and having different names for different variations is a step toward that goal.

What is a significant redesign? Adding a Flipgrid to the reflection portion of the Cyber Sandwich is an excellent idea if it meets curricular goals; however, it is not a significant redesign and therefore does not warrant a new name. Removing the Venn diagram and replacing it with three new steps that are entirely different from those in the original Cyber Sandwich would be a significant enough redesign to justify a new name.

When Kevin Feramisco (@theteachingjedi) and his students blended the Iron Chef EduProtocol and the Frayer EduProtocol into one activity, the natural choice for a new name was the Iron Chef Frayer EduProtocol. Combining the names of the protocols points the students to two activities they already know and lets them easily deduce what the new activity will look like: an Iron Chef using a Frayer!

Let the Fun Begin!

Educators share their remixed EduProtocol creations with us all the time, and we love seeing how teachers are using them to engage students! If you're inspired to create new variations, please share them with us using #EduProtocols on Twitter, or you can use the contact form available on eduprotocols.com to reach Jon or Marlena.

Call to Action

Seasoned User

If you have been using EduProtocols in your classroom or with students, share some of your iterations and ideas on Twitter for others to enjoy.

New to EduProtocols?

If you are new to using EduProtocols, check out what other teachers are doing at eduprotocols.com (look for samples on the templates pages) or on Twitter with #EduProtocols.

Jeremiah took over for a middle school teacher in the middle of the school year. The biggest struggle that the students had was putting their learning together to accomplish a task. These eighth graders were supposed to be in the middle of solving systems of equations and seemed to be cursed with disorganized thinking and confusion between the various methods. So the first week that he was their teacher, Jeremiah gave them a simplified MathRep solution with all three methods and a guess-and-check style problem for a simple word problem. They practiced the same scenario every day for that first week; each day, he reduced the time that he allocated to the MathRep by five minutes, from thirty minutes on Monday to ten minutes by Friday. Jeremiah wasn't pressuring students to finish in a certain amount of time, but as students became more proficient, they completed the MathReps with confidence.

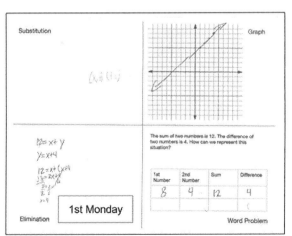
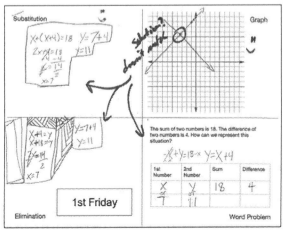

The student barely understood the task and concepts on Monday. By Friday, the student began to connect the substitution of numbers for x and y.

At the end of the week their growth was substantial, as illustrated by the work of a student on an Individualized Education Plan (IEP) in the example above.

With another group of students, using a MathRep for a linear models, Jeremiah tracked each student's performance over three different ways of solving the unit fraction and the equivalent fraction representations. Over three months, students across multiple school sites went from no student scoring above 50 percent to no student scoring less than 75 percent. Considering many of these students began with negative feelings regarding mathematics, feeling successful and capable due to the combination of support in their conceptual understanding and frequent practice with MathReps created a powerful learning experience for them!

Academic Goals:

- Students gain confidence with essential skills to make way for more in-depth learning.
- Spiral review of previously learned concepts.
- Algorithmic skills learned in prior grades linked to current concept development.

Math Practices:

- CCSS MATH PRACTICE: MP1: Make sense of problems and persevere in solving them.
- CCSS MATH PRACTICE: MP2: Reason abstractly and quantitatively.
- CCSS MATH PRACTICE: MP5: Use appropriate tools strategically.
- CCSS MATH PRACTICE: MP6: Attend to precision.

Teacher Big Ideas:

- Mastery of math concepts is the main focus of MathReps.
- Build conceptual understanding before introducing the MathRep.
- Build class-wide camaraderie by creating a culture in which the class achieves together while tracking progress individually.

Description:

A MathRep is an activity in which students take a number through a series of concepts and standards at one time. A key element is *creating cohesion within a strand of algorithmic skills.* For example, provided with the number 25, students generate a decimal, a fraction, and a graphic of the fraction for the integer; place it on a number line; and find place value to the 10th, 100th, 1,000th, etc.

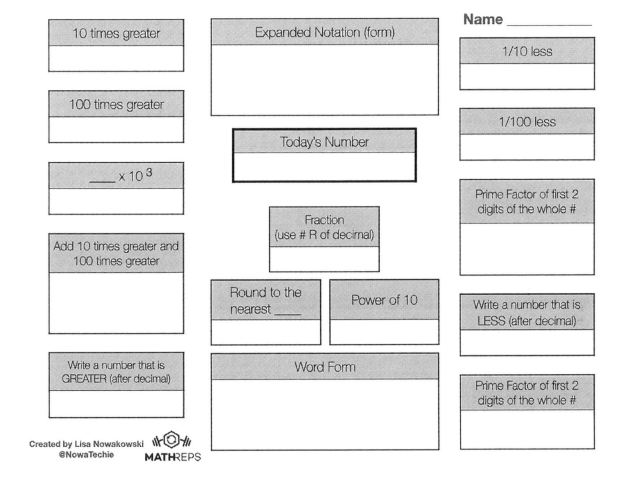

In this example, start with writing today's number in the center box. Project the MathRep so that students can follow along. Fill it in as they copy. From there, fill in expanded form and word form. Move to the left side of the paper and fill it in, taking time to show and do quick reviews on the most confusing parts. Finally, move on to the right side of the paper. You may have noticed that we skipped a few concepts in the middle column. For many students, those concepts tend to be a bit more confusing; try skipping them the first few times you demonstrate the MathRep. In this manner, we scale up students' skill level in practicing the execution of the connected strand of algorithmic skills.

Prepare for the Activity:

Step 1: Choose or create your MathRep. Using your math framework of standards to locate grade level strands of algorithmic skills is a great place to start!

Step 2: Look closely at your chosen MathRep. Which areas will students complete with you first? Roughly schedule out how much they will do each day with you.

Instructions:

Step 1: Deploy your MathRep either through paper copies or digitally. Complete the entire MathRep the first time you introduce it. Work through each of the boxes together; provide the answers in the beginning. Students will eventually do the entire page in one sitting.

Consider jumping right in with students and work to complete the entire MathRep. Constructivism is a lesson design theory in which learners tackle the whole and then, through repetition, achieve mastery. Since the MathRep does not generally contain concepts new to students, a quick start accomplishes a few goals:

- Provides an excellent review at the beginning of the year for everyone. Many may have forgotten how to solve the problems.
- Allows students to feel safe.
- Helps to build a culture of community because we are all in this together.

Step 2: Execute your plan and get to work! Keep in mind student attention spans and know when to stop for the day.

MathReps can be challenging, and it is better to accomplish less while ending on a positive note.

Step 3: Repeat several times during the week.

On Day 1, spoon-feed your students. By Day 5, challenge students to do a few of the concepts on their own.

Many students take an opportunity to look back at previously completed work and copy. Students try to do it on the sly because they think they'll get in trouble for looking back! Another tactic that they try is to ask a neighbor—again, trying to do it in secret. Pretend not to see them looking back at completed papers or hear them talking to one another! By the second week, feel free to openly encourage them to partake in such behaviors.

Step 4: When students have mastered a particular MathRep paper, move on to a new one and the process will start all over. However, once students have the flow of the new MathRep, cycle back to a previous one so they do not forget the prior skills. When your students are ready for a break from practicing current skills, this is an easy way to build in a review! You will most likely find that they have forgotten a few of the concepts. No worries—by the end of the week the students will have it mastered once again! Do this a few times with each of the MathReps throughout the year.

Note: *There will be times when moving on to the next MathReps may not be an option! One year, Lisa had a student that was never able to complete the MathRep, no matter how many times they tried. In cases like that, work with the student and any IEPs in place to modify the goal. Consider breaking the task into parts and use practice over time (i.e., distributed practice) to build skills. Digital MathReps can be easily used and deployed for differentiation.*

Jon

We call all these reps. And as every athlete knows, reps are essential for mastery.

Name:	Period: Group: **Math Reps: Parallel Lines & Transversals**	
m ∠ 2 =	**Angles Congruent to ∠1:**	**Corresponding Angles Pairs:**
m ∠ 3=	**Angles Supplementary to ∠1:**	
m ∠ 4=	**Today's Parallel Lines & Transversals Diagram:**	**Alternate Interior Angle Pairs:**
m ∠ 5=	m ∠ 1=_____ a // b	
m ∠ 6=		**Alternate Exterior Angle Pairs:**
m ∠ 7=	(diagram: angles 1 8 / 2 7 on line a; 3 6 / 4 5 on line b)	
m ∠ 8=		**Same Side Interior Angle Pairs:**
Linear Pairs	**Vertical Angle Pairs:**	

@Kristanmorales1   MATHREPS

MathReps can be used across mathematics curriculums and grade levels.

Key Points to Remember:

- Distributed practice allows for synthesis over time.
- Build team spirit among your students: post the progress and percentage as a class and *never* as individuals.
- Sometimes paper works better.
- Immediate feedback is essential. No matter how many times we do a MathReps paper, check it together daily. Collect the papers when both sides are filled up. Then do a spot check by picking one concept to check on everyone's paper. This check allows time to see who is completing the work or just copying.

Adaptations for Primary Students:

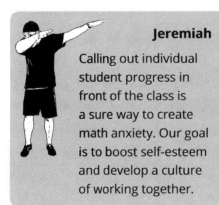

Second-grade MathRep reinforcing number sense in a variety of ways.

Young students tend to move quickly through a one-page MathRep, so consider stacking a few slides together to keep them moving along. Plan your MathRep to cover the skills you have worked on in the past or are working on currently. In the sample above, Meghan Cannon-Johann uses MathReps for practicing money counting and writing skills.

Pro Tips:

When a student is working ahead of the class and can successfully master the current MathReps assessment two weeks in a row, allow that student to create tutorials. Have them take the assessment each week but allow them to skip the daily review. Easily create tutorials using Flipgrid or Screencastify. Students work on alternate tasks while the others are working on their daily MathReps. Or, allow these students to create MathReps on their own!

To streamline checking papers for 150 students, push out a five-day template through Google Classroom or Microsoft Teams. As their weekly "quiz," students write on the fifth blank slide a para-

Jeremiah

Calling out individual student progress in front of the class is a sure way to create math anxiety. Our goal is to boost self-esteem and develop a culture of working together.

Marlena

Growing the entire class to mastery and feeling good about it is a huge Social Emotional Learning (SEL) value-added component of EduProtocols.

graph describing how they saw their growth change over the week and share what they thought was still not "sticky" for them. Use this information to design future review of material that students do not feel they mastered.

If you use Google Slides to create your MathReps, use master slides to edit the background of the slide. This way, students will not disrupt the basic structure of the MathRep. Remember to place manipulatives on the surface of the slide.

Easily differentiate instruction for the whole class or for individuals by dragging boxes that students are not ready to complete off the side of the slide until you are ready to include them.

When moving from paper to technology-embedded, allow students the choice to continue on paper if they so desire. It's okay if that is more comfortable for them. Consider having students turn in an image of their MathRep to your digital LMS or Google Classroom.

For some MathReps, paper and pencil is the best method. Students often struggle with lining up numbers or regrouping, and they need practice with this skill. We may live in a digital age, but we need to make technology fit the task. Sometimes that means going old school.

For primary students, you may want to remove certain concepts and boxes, introducing new concepts one at one time as you build up to the whole. Slowly scaling up will allow primary students to stay focused and not become overwhelmed as they learn the technology while practicing the math. Scaling up also allows for pacing with the curriculum so that concepts are added to the MathRep after the conceptual learning phase.

Lisa

I won't lie to you: the first time you do this it will take a long time. You will wonder if it will take as long each time. You will wonder if this is worth it. The answers are simple: no, and ***absolutely*** YES!

Find the MathRep collection of pre-made MathReps for all grade levels at bit.ly/mathreps.

Chapter 7

The Fast and Curious Facts EduProtocol

Beating your own score is irresistible to kids, and beating your class score is even better! In this EduProtocol students follow a three-step process using a quiz program such as Quizizz: take the quiz, review the answers, and immediately take the test again. Repeat for a few days and watch the magic happen! Use this mini-EduProtocol to help students memorize math facts and vocabulary.

Academic Goals:

- Memorize concepts and vocabulary.
- Provide for quick repetitions of content.
- Targeted skill practice.

Math Practices:

- CCSS MATH PRACTICE: MP1: Make sense of problems and persevere in solving them.
- CCSS MATH PRACTICE: MP6: Attend to precision.

Teacher Big Ideas:

- Turn a not-so-fun task into something that engages students.
- Build confidence.
- It takes repetition to build mastery.

Description:

In The Fast and Curious Facts, teachers use a quiz program such as Quizizz to help students develop mastery. This EduProtocol works well for vocabulary as well as developing *automaticity* with math facts—without the stigma of timed math when student-controlled and -directed (see Variations below).

The Fast and Curious has three distinct parts:

1. Students take the quiz.
2. The teacher reviews the questions and the answers with the class. (When used for math fact practice, this is different. See below for the math fact practice modification.)
3. The students retake the quiz.

Consider the middle step for a moment. We are giving students the answers! Giving the answer is what differentiates The Fast and Curious from tests and removes the stigma of testing. Little do students realize that the two-round process is what is helping them to remember! The whole class average for the *second round* is written on the board each time as the score to beat, keeping the focus on *class gains and teambuilding.*

Why do kids love The Fast and Curious? It is irresistible when students are presented with the challenge of beating their collective class score. And for classroom culture, nothing beats winning week after week to bolster classroom morale.

Prepare for the Activity:

To prepare for this activity, make an account in a quiz program such as Quizizz. Become familiar with using the program and making quizzes. In many quiz programs there will be a library of user-created quizzes that may be copied and reused. This is a great way to find quizzes quickly. Try searching with the name of your story, textbook, or curriculum area to find ready-made quizzes.

Marlena

Kids and adults really do love this protocol. It's called The Fast and Curious because we are always curious if we can beat ourselves!

Jon

Attempting to beat our own score is irresistible!

Instructions:

Step 1: Set up an account with an online gaming review site, such as Quizizz, and log in.

Step 2: Create a quiz for the math facts of your choice OR find one from the quiz program library!

Step 3: Start a game.

Step 4: Instruct students on joining the game.

Step 5: When all students are in, begin the game.

Step 6: As students are finishing up, note the score on the board as the score to beat next time.

Step 7: Review the vocabulary after everyone has finished.

Step 8: Allow students to retake the quiz and note the new score on the board as the score to beat the following day.

Repeat the game daily and try to beat the class average each time you play. Minimize focus on individual scores, although it is helpful for students to note their individual scores so they can monitor their progress. If students track and maintain their score records and know that the teacher does not monitor these, the responsibility for achievement shifts to the student.

Jeremiah

When I first tried FAC, I was nervous my kids wouldn't like that we were using it for skill building. After one rep, the kids were dying to try again and again and again; that is when I knew this was a powerful tool for learning.

Lisa

I was VERY skeptical of using this EduProtocol for math fact fluency. The latest research is clear that timed tests do more harm than good. However, I gave it a try. My kiddos LOVED it. The best part was that one student in my class who was struggling voluntarily took the quiz two and sometimes three times in an attempt to get a perfect score. So she was practicing twice as much as the rest of the class. A few students caught on that someone was taking it more than once. At first, they were upset; they didn't see it as being fair. Once I explained that she was doing twice as much work as others, we celebrated her and her determination. It doesn't hurt that I've gamified it. There were perks for getting 100 percent. The class is so focused on doing well that they helped one another.

We beat our score!

Variations:

Too many times, we have heard teachers lament about their students not knowing their math facts, thus hindering their ability to complete tasks successfully. We also know that timed tests don't work because the anxiety creates a negative effect on fact fluency, even for high-achieving math students. Timed math tests contribute to the myth that if you are fast, you are good at math, which is not true for many students. Taking all that into consideration, we suggest using The Fast and Curious EduProtocol to allow students to have agency in their own math practice, therefore eliminating timed math performance. There are a few tricks to accomplish this. First, remember that the practice is for improving fluency and automaticity, not for concept development. Next, let students have choice in the order of the math facts being practiced. Finally, expect students to do the tracking, not the teacher. This allows student agency over the learning, which is crucial for mastery of math facts.

Jeremiah

When students own and have control over their destiny, competition against oneself is not anxiety-inducing!

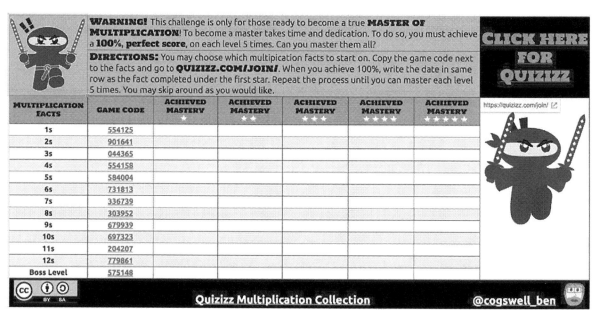

WARNING! This challenge is only for those ready to become a true **MASTER OF MULTIPLICATION!** To become a master takes time and dedication. To do so, you must achieve a **100%, perfect score**, on each level 5 times. Can you master them all?

DIRECTIONS: You may choose which multipication facts to start on. Copy the game code next to the facts and go to **QUIZIZZ.COM/JOIN/**. When you achieve 100%, write the date in same row as the fact completed under the first star. Repeat the process until you can master each level 5 times. You may skip around as you would like.

CLICK HERE FOR QUIZIZZ

https://quizizz.com/join/

MULTIPLICATION FACTS	GAME CODE	ACHIEVED MASTERY ★	ACHIEVED MASTERY ★ ★	ACHIEVED MASTERY ★ ★ ★	ACHIEVED MASTERY ★ ★ ★ ★	ACHIEVED MASTERY ★ ★ ★ ★ ★
1s	554125					
2s	901641					
3s	044365					
4s	554158					
5s	584004					
6s	731813					
7s	336739					
8s	303952					
9s	679939					
10s	697323					
11s	204207					
12s	779861					
Boss Level	575148					

Quizizz Multiplication Collection   **@cogswell_ben**

Ben Cogswell demonstrates this beautifully in his multiplication math fact tracking sheet in the image above. Students decide what to practice and have the full range of choices; they master that deck five times before choosing another deck. The timing on these decks allows plenty of time, to remove the timed math pressure. Students complete the tracking on their own sheet and these sheets are not displayed publicly. Once kids own their learning—achieved by allowing students to manage their learning by setting goals and navigating through the learning—math fact fluency and automaticity becomes more accessible.

Key Points to Remember:

- Keep it fun to build confidence!
- Focus on class growth for vocabulary.
- Focus on individual growth for math facts.
- There are many quiz options available that work wonderfully!

Adaptations for Primary Students:

Use The Fast and Curious to identify shapes, numbers matched to sets of objects, lots of vocabulary, object/name recognition such as number words matched to numbers, etc. Allow plenty of time if students are reading. For non-readers, make your Fast and Curious without words or with few words, as this is a self-paced quiz and the teacher will not be able to read the questions aloud. Other quiz programs allow for class pacing and may also be used.

Pro Tip: Set your quiz program, like Quizizz, to homework, and then allow students to take their quiz at will. Many teachers set up a "must do" and a "may do" list that allows for independence and choice.

Lisa

Monday was our first day back after a three-week winter break. As we do regularly, we practiced our math facts using the Fast and Curious EduProtocol. I had anticipated a drop from our usual 96 to 98 percent. I predicted, to myself, it would drop to around 89 percent. I wasn't too concerned as I knew that they could easily get it back up to our normal average within a week. Well, to my surprise, my class scored  94 percent. Seriously, I was happily surprised that they really didn't lose as much as I had feared. YES! The continuous rep practice has worked. The facts are sticking.

Chapter 8
Frayer Math EduProtocol

The Frayer Math EduProtocol is a simple but powerful conceptual development tool. Use it when you want students to develop a deeper understanding of content. We love using the Frayer model for vocabulary! The versatility of this simple tool will allow you to apply it to your curriculum in a few different ways—and you might come up with some of your own adaptations, too!

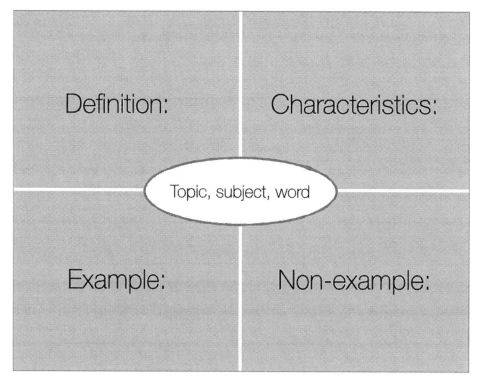

Math Vocabulary Frayer

Academic Goals:

- Develop understanding of words or concepts.
- Create a simple graphic organizer that students can replicate on their own.
- Make learning and memorizing attainable when appropriate.

Math Practices:

- CCSS MATH PRACTICE: MP1: Make sense of problems and persevere in solving them.
- CCSS MATH PRACTICE: MP5: Use appropriate tools strategically.
- CCSS MATH PRACTICE: MP6: Attend to precision.
- CCSS MATH PRACTICE: MP7: Look for and make use of structure.

Teacher Big Ideas:

- Simple.
- Easy to replicate.
- Facilitates deeper understandings.
- Frayers make great study tools!

Description:

Originally created by Dorothy Frayer and her colleagues at the University of Wisconsin in the 1960s, the Frayer is a five-square graphic organizer used for teaching word analysis and building vocabulary. Sonny Magana explains the difference between a worksheet and a graphic organizer: "The worksheet narrows down to only one possible correct answer and is therefore convergent. The graphic organizer allows for many possible solutions and thereby allows for divergent thinking for each student." The Frayer is a beautiful example of how to honor divergent thinking.

The Frayer is organized into five areas. The center area contains the vocabulary word and the remaining boxes are divided into definition, characteristics of the definition, an example, and a

Jon

When students have devices in hand, Frayer Models are like repeatable, super-quick scavenger hunts. Open-ended and with fast feedback, the Frayer is a powerful learning concept.

non-example. Notice the nuances of using the terms *example* and *non-example* over synonym and antonym. These two simple words allow for the Frayer to be used beyond word definitions and expands its use into a powerful concept development tool.

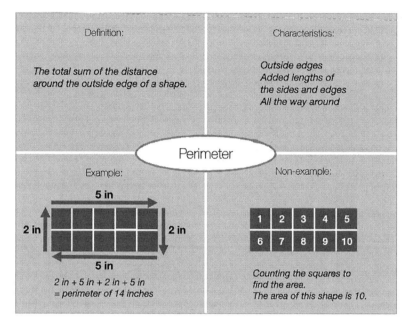

The Math Frayer EduProtocol is extremely adaptable based on the needs of the students.

Prepare for the Activity:

Prepare the Frayer model by creating the five-square template as shown below in a paper or electronic format—Google or PowerPoint slides work well for the Frayer. Students or the teacher labels the center square with the concept or vocabulary word. In the four outer boxes, add titles: definition, characteristics, example, and non-example.

Instructions:

Step 1: Prepare and distribute the Frayer to students in digital or paper format.

Step 2: Allow students time to work on the Frayer. The amount of time you provide for students will vary depending on students' age and their task. Remember, just the right amount of time—not too much and not too little.

Step 3: Students complete the four outer boxes in the Frayer: definition, characteristics, examples, and non-examples.

Step 4: Deepen conceptual understanding by allowing students time to present their completed Frayers to their peers.

Variations:

VERSION 1: The Frayer may be used in the manner of the original Iron Chef, in which four students work in teams to build Frayers for four or more vocabulary words. This slide deck then becomes a study tool for students.

Lisa

When I first saw Jeremiah present this, using quadrants, I had a "That's BRILLIANT!" moment. What a great way to ease students into the understanding of quadrants.

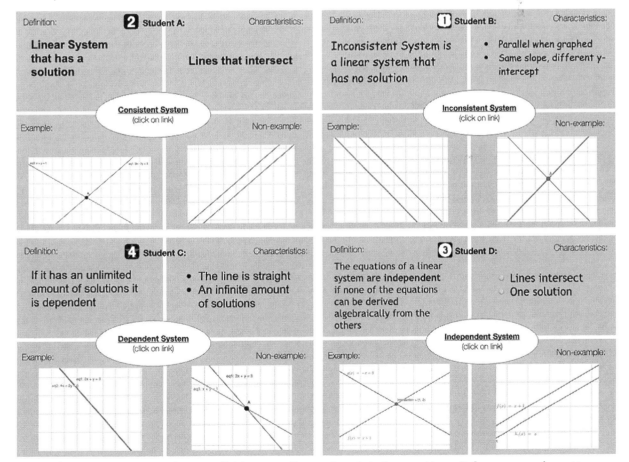

The intersecting x- and y-axes divide a coordinate plane into four sections. Reference your layouts using the academic language of quadrants 1–4 so that students learn this terminology.

VERSION 2: Number the paper like a coordinate plane (as in the image below) with each quadrant number representing the four components of the Frayer. When speaking with students, refer to the quadrants to help students become familiar with this space (quadrant 1, quadrant, 2, quadrant 3, or quadrant 4) long before they reach the graphing stage in advanced math classes. You will notice many of the examples in this book numbered in this manner.

When assigning students to collaboratively work on one Frayer, preassign the quadrant number for each student by assigning them numbers 1 to 4, and then have each student complete the quadrant of their corresponding number. Then have the students synthesize the entire learning for that particular content.

VERSION 3: The Frayer can be used in a math modeling experience in which each square is designated as a different way to model mathematics. The teacher may dictate the method used for each box, or students may be allowed to choose the method for showing a solution in each box.

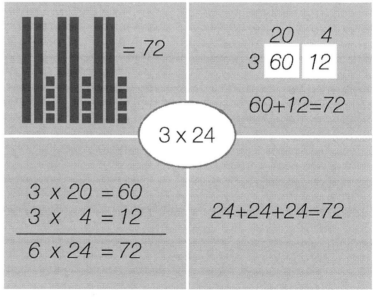

The basic structure of the five-box Frayer is used
to solve 3 x 24 in four different ways

Get the Frayer Icon Board Template at
bit.ly/frayer-eduprotocol-icon-board

VERSION 4: Another example comes from a single adaptation of Iron Chef, where students work with a resource to complete a slide. Supply a resource link in the center of the slide set up as a Frayer. The student determines the information for each of the quadrants from the provided resource. The student is constructing their understanding of the concept; their responses act as a formative assessment on what the student is learning.

In the example below, the students will represent the fraction in the center using the model identified for each quadrant. The clickable URL in each quadrant has an example for students to follow, should they need the support. Students take a few minutes to finish their contribution, and then the group is given a few more minutes to make connections between the various representations. The final wrinkle is a random call from a random number generator set from 1 to 4, and each group's member of that number rises to share out their problem and connections. Depending on the topic and the class, every group may have the same problem or concept, or they may all have different issues or ideas and the class has to determine how these pieces fit together.

Set Model ②	Numerator	Denominator	① Linear Model
tinyurl.com/yalvzryf			tinyurl.com/y7dh6l4n
tinyurl.com/yanbq22h	$\dfrac{6}{9}$		tinyurl.com/yb52wdza
	Compare < > =	Unit Fraction	□/□ = □/□
Area Model ③			④ Equivalent Fractions

🐦 @mathkaveli

Marlena

When my daughter was struggling in her second year of college calculus, a wise professor told her to solve the same problem in as many different ways as she possibly could. Her understanding of math, as well as her scores, increased immediately! Why? She developed a deeper understanding of how the math worked together as a whole.

Everyone in the class can work on the same problem. The advantage of this is that the students who are all working on one method can join forces. Collaboration!

- Conversely, you can have each group work on a different problem. The advantage of this is that the class can hear and see how the same process works for different sets of problems.
- If each student is only doing one quadrant, consider pairing a struggling student with a stronger one to work out the problem together. Remember to assign the quadrants to the students using the method in Modification 1.

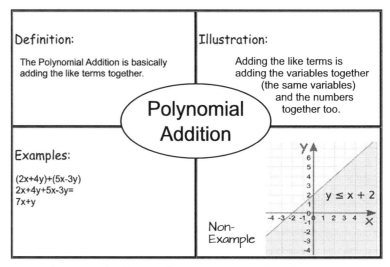

The example above is from an Integrated Math 3 course Jeremiah taught as they were entering the operations of polynomials unit. This was an introductory activity that students used for each of the operations.

VERSION 5: When using the Frayer to model mathematics, add other features like multiple Notice and Wonder prompts and various ways to encourage students to consider the multiple representations in which a problem might appear.

Show an image, a sequence of sentences, or a video in a sequence and ask the students to write what they notice and what they wonder at each pause. Each cycle as the option for students to utilize a Turn and Talk, sharing their observations, and occasionally asking for someone to share out with the whole class. This slow release allows the students to make sense of the problem so that they can tackle it more efficiently when they flip the Frayer model over and begin to solve.

Jeremiah

The Frayer model was my first journey into Math EduProtocols, as the Frayer structure reminds me of a coordinate plane. More importantly, the Frayer is a really great way to have fun and give students meaningful access to mathematics, and really embraces that EduProtocol philosophy: one structure, infinite learning possibilities.

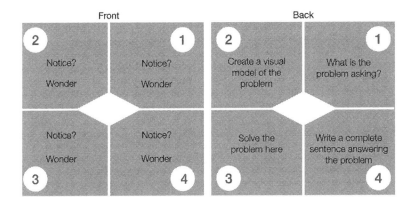

Key Point to Remember:

- The best non-examples are the ones easily confused with the example. We would use the example "area" and the non-example "perimeter": two easily confused concepts. We would not use the example "area" and non-example "microwave," which is what kids will start with until you guide them into better non-examples.

Adaptations for Primary Students:

Drawing programs such as Google Drawing make excellent work mats for students to visualize simple work. Provide counters and manipulatives, including numbers, embedded in the drawing or slide to allow students to drag and drop to show their thinking instead of creating from scratch. This approach works well for all age groups

Pro Tip: Drag-and-drop numbers and math symbols make this protocol a snap online.

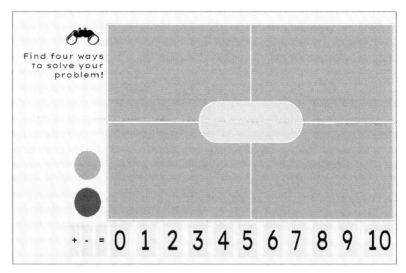

Find this template at bit.ly/frayer-math-rep-eduprotocol

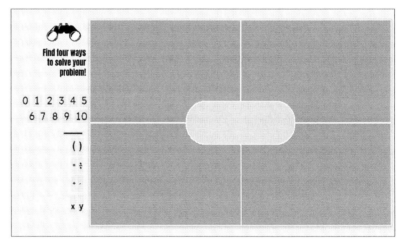

The Frayer Icon Board allows students to drag and drop numbers and symbols in addition to using text boxes to make their thinking visible.

Chapter 9

The Math Sous Chef EduProtocol

In the Math Sous Chef EduProtocol, groups of four students complete a four-slide jigsaw of a math problem or concept utilizing the natural scaffold and collaboration that peers can provide. The Math Sous Chef EduProtocol is a math adaptation of the original Iron Chef EduProtocol that has been used by teachers in every grade and in just about every subject across the country. This application in math allows students to collaborate with peers in learning and in preparing math problems for solving. Unlike the original Iron Chef, the Math Sous Chef is not timed, is open-ended, and allows students to see problems from more than one perspective—just like the second-in-command in the kitchen, the Sous Chef!

Academic Goals:

- Increase and improve understanding.
- Develop number sense and fluency.
- Make thinking visible.

Math Practices:

- CCSS MATH PRACTICE: MP1: Make sense of problems and persevere in solving them.
- CCSS MATH PRACTICE: MP5: Use appropriate tools strategically.
- CCSS MATH PRACTICE: MP7: Look for and make use of structure.

Teacher Big Ideas:

- If you have been using EduProtocols in your classroom, you may find that students are already familiar with this one; if so, the learning will be accelerated.
- Unlike the original Iron Chef EduProtocol published in *The EduProtocol Field Guide, Book 1*, this one for math is un-timed.
- Collaboration is to be encouraged.
- Provide feedback to students in real-time.
- Refer to a DOK (Depth of Knowledge) Chart for prompts for the secret ingredient question. The same prompt may be used for all students.

Description:

The original Iron Chef was designed to place students in charge of their learning. This gamified jigsaw has students collaborating, creating, presenting, and actively listening. Students are directed to create one slide on a specific topic (resource provided) with three to four bullet points of information and one image. (For more information, see *EduProtocols Field Guide, Book 1*, chapter 26.) Sous Chef is based on this model. The teacher can choose different models to use depending on focus—developing under-standing of different methods to solve or everyone practicing a newer method. No matter which model the teacher chooses, the students are in charge, working collaboratively. Students create, present, and actively listen. By listening, the students are reinforc-ing concepts and methods, thus deepening their understanding. As in the original Iron Chef EduProtocol, there is a "secret ingredi-ent." It could be a fun question related to the topic, the definition of a vocabulary word, or it could ask students to apply their math knowledge to a real-world example.

Prepare for the Activity:

Use The Math Sous Chef weekly to allow students to master the format of this EduProtocol. For the most success with The Math

Sous Chef, commit to using it all year long. You'll see the maximum impact after at least ten rounds. The teacher prepares a slide deck and shares it with groups of four students. The students complete the prompt for their slide.

In the original Iron Chef, time is of the essence. However, now that we are armed with the knowledge that timed math produces math anxiety, we believe you should restrict the use of the original Iron Chef EduProtocol as a timed activity for conceptual understanding and vocabulary development only. Use the new reformatted Sous Chef EduProtocol for working problems, as we have shown in some of the examples. Be very aware of the damage that timed activities inflict upon students and steer away from this application. Gently guide students to a ten- to fifteen-minute build time. Keep the task simple enough to allow completion in this short amount of time.

High school students working diligently on their Math Sous Chef.

The Math Sous Chef Consists of These Elements:

- Three to four students work as a team and may help each other.
- Three to four slides, each with a different topic, vocabulary word, prompt, or method of displaying a problem.
- When using this protocol for math-related activities, skip the timer. You can still gauge about ten minutes for building, but don't pressure kids to complete in a specified amount of time. If kids are taking longer than ten minutes, consider shorter prompts or break prompts into smaller parts.
- Upon completion of The Math Sous Chef, students present briefly to the class or group (one minute per student).
- Make sure that the components stand alone. The Math Sous Chef is a type of jigsaw, which means that it does not work well when breaking apart passages that build, as the last group will not have the background to understand that last part if they did not read the first part!
- Each slide has a "secret ingredient" that engages the early finisher and contributes to teamwork in completing the entire slide deck. The secret ingredient is part of the overall task and might include areas of interest that are related to the main topic. Secret ingredients may be an extension of The Math Sous Chef, or they may not be related at all. The DOK Chart will give you key words to build a higher-level thinking question for your students. Other examples may include:
  - a word problem for the math concept just explained
  - a real-life example
  - a drawing to illustrate a math concept (perhaps an extension of a math problem being studied or a review concept)
  - the definition of a math vocabulary word
  - steps to a process (for example, the order of operations)
  - problems or common confusion that people might encounter

How do you know if a topic is a good fit for The Math Sous Chef? If the answer is mostly text, or bulleted text, or an image that students create, then likely the item is a good fit. The Math Sous Chef can also be used to chunk information in the textbook that students are reading. If each reading selection can stand independently from the others, then it will work in The Math Sous Chef.

Other Ideas:

- For kindergarten- Things that are made from specific shapes: wheels and pie plates are like circles; windows and game boards are like rectangles.
- Explain the order of operations.
- How to measure different types of angles.
- Give the answer! Provide students a problem and the answer. Students will demonstrate different ways to display the problem. For example: Represent 35 + 12 = 47.
  - Student 1: Using base ten blocks
  - Student 2: Using a ten frame
  - Student 3: Using decomposition addition or expanded form
  - Student 4: Using a four square

Instructions:

Step 1: Prepare and distribute The Math Sous Chef slide deck to student leaders.

Step 2: Student leaders share the deck with their team members.

Step 3: Allow approximately ten minutes for students to work on their slides and adjust time for the needs of the group. Note: If you are finding that students need more than ten to fifteen minutes, consider smaller or less complicated prompts for your next round. Don't extend this ten- to fifteen-minute work time; shorten the prompt.

Step 4: When the build time is completed, students present their slides. This presenting step is important to allow students time to share their thinking. Presenting can be as formal

Lisa

Whether assigning the task for all or not, be sensitive to all students. Some students will need to be challenged, whereas others will need help.

Jeremiah

The beautiful thing about this EduProtocol is that its iterations and content are often only limited by our own imagination.

Marlena

If a group of students is especially struggling with finishing, try giving them a head start or meeting with them before class begins to go over the tasks that they will be completing.

Jon

Be aware of getting pulled into the "suck," where the time to work far exceeds the time that is necessary to complete the task.

or as informal as you wish: choose two groups to present, allow groups of two to present to each other, or one group can present to the remaining members within that group.

Assign the slide decks through your Google Classroom or LMS and when presentations are to be to the whole class, navigate to the grading window and project from there. The grading window will allow you to easily navigate between groups and students, making presentation quicker and easier!

Allow students a few minutes to gather their thoughts, practice a run-through, or make notes on what they will say. Assist students that need support. Allow students to opt out of presenting to the whole class or to present in less intimidating intimate groups. Most of all, keep it fun! Kids learn more when the atmosphere is joyous!

Step 5: Bonus round! Allow all students an additional five minutes to adjust their own slide after the presentation round. After all, they may have learned a few tips from watching their peers.

Variations:

There are several variations of this EduProtocol. Play around with it and find what works for you and your students.

VERSION 1: Consider the organization of the jigsaw aspect of The Math Sous Chef when working with different types of problems. There are several possibilities that will change the way the work comes together and how students collaborate together.

Type of Grouping	Four Students	Four Students	Four Students
Number of problems for the group	Same problem for all	Same problem for all	Four different problems
Student Task	Solve using four different methods	Solve using the same method	Solve using four different methods

Experiment, see what works with your students, and mix it up to keep it fresh!

VERSION 2: The entire class works on the same prompt and each student creates just one slide. Each slide contains the bare minimum in response to a prompt. In the original Thin Slides from the *EduProtocol Field Guide, Book 2*, the Thin Slide contains one image and one word. To develop number sense and math concepts, more than one word and one image might be needed. As an adaptation of The Math Sous Chef, the Thin Slide might be a little less thin, but keep it to the minimum! Tip: Sometimes it is easier to assign one slide per student than to have all students working on the same slide deck. The advantage of one deck is that students can see the work of their peers. Take the time to teach the skills (respecting each other's work) to be able to have the class work on one slide deck all at once.

VERSION 3: When using this activity for vocabulary, revert back to the original timed version of Iron Chef, which was made for just this kind of thing! Consider inserting a Vocabulary Frayer template (see Frayer Math, chapter 8) into the Iron Chef to help students organize their work.

VERSION 4: The Math Frayer also makes a useful addition to The Math Sous Chef. Students are not solving the problem in this version; they are modeling the problem four different ways to study the modeling and to deepen their understanding of the math. This is a useful tool that can be used to scaffold the abilities of students within a group while making every member of the group feel that they are valuable contributors.

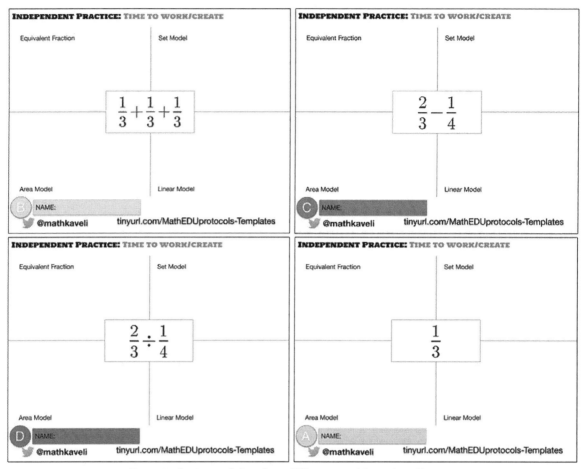

Four students modeling four different problems in a Frayer
that is being used in The Math Sous Chef style.

Key Points to Remember:

- You know your learners best; watch for signs of stress and make accommodations accordingly, especially if they are familiar with the prior structure of the original timed Iron Chef.

- Keep presentations moving along. One minute per student is enough. Most students will present in even less time.

- Be aware that pressure to perform in front of the class may cause math anxiety in some. Be very sensitive to this even if students are not working problems; just the fact that the topic is math-related may mean that some students have brought a level of anxiety with them, and it can manifest in different ways.

- Be flexible. In Lisa's class, one student didn't like the secret ingredient (find an example in the real world) and wrote her own word problem. This is a fantastic idea for the secret ingredient.

Adaptations for Primary Students:

- Younger learners may prefer to work together in pairs.
- Manipulatives, including movable numbers, on the page make work faster for young students.
- Keeping the content at grade level is what makes this Edu-Protocol work with younger students.
- Create groups in your Google or Microsoft Classrooms so that the sharing is done by the teacher instead of by the students.
- A quick practice and prep before presenting goes a long way with kids, allow opting out of presenting, or allow presenting in less intimidating intimate groups.
- Use "turn and present." Have students turn to a partner and present. Or, one group may present to another group.
- Any of the versions above can be used with younger learners; the scaffolding happens when you insert grade appropriate content.

Pro Tip: *To be sensitive to students who may have math anxiety, allow volunteers to present first so that less confident students are more familiar with the concepts before they present. Or direct one group to present to another group, instead of to the whole class. And always be sensitive and adjust to an individual student's needs. Jon awards bonus points to teams that volunteer to go first.*

Chapter 10
3-Act Math® EduProtocol

The 3-Act Math® EduProtocol uses a video, demonstration, or image as a hook to spark student's curiosity about a mathematical concept. The hook is intended to leave a particular thought to be desired (more on this soon). Once the class has seen Act 1, the hook, Act 2 is focused on getting to the crux of the problem at hand, with math serving as the vehicle toward a possible solution. Act 3 is the reveal: the end of the video or demonstration, or revealing the next part of the image to verify the work that has been done.

About the Creator:

John Stevens is an instructional coach and author of *Table Talk Math* and coauthor of *The Classroom Chef*. Here he explains the process of Dan Meyer's 3-Act Math process.

Academic Goals:

- Develop prioritization skills.
- Enhance problem-solving skills in mathematics.
- Make students curious about a common problem or idea.

Math Practices:

- CCSS MATH PRACTICE: MP1: Make sense of problems and persevere in solving them.
- CCSS MATH PRACTICE: MP5: Use appropriate tools strategically.
- CCSS MATH PRACTICE: MP6: Attend to precision.
- CCSS MATH PRACTICE: MP7: Look for and make use of structure.

Teacher Big Ideas:

- Find a piece of media that has a good hook.
- Pause/edit the media at the point where the mathematics will help.
- Encourage student curiosity and exploration.

Description:

Here, John Stevens describes how he uses 3-Act Math®:

As with most new activities, we recommend trying a 3-Act task and taking time to reflect on the experience. When I first started using dynamic lessons in math class, I immediately wanted to do more, then quickly became overwhelmed, then stopped. I know, I know—and that's why I emphasize the need for reflection, which is easily overlooked. If all I'm really doing is scouring the internet for awesome content and delivering it, the reality is that I'm not growing as a professional. While channeling content is okay at first, push yourself to reflect on why these ideas work, how you would change them, and what impact they have on your students.

Once you understand the format of a 3-Act task, my recommendation to teachers is to aim for one per week, or three in a two-week span, eventually getting into a weekly rhythm. Doing tasks like these every day will overwhelm the students, so splitting them up is good for all parties.

The big thing I'm working to avoid is a one-and-done approach where I will try out a task, like it, then shelve the concept for the remainder of the year.

Instructions:

Step 1: Find the Right Video

Popularized by Dan Meyer, 3-Act Math® tasks are fun to do with students but can be intimidating to create by your-

Marlena

Since there is no such thing as "just" a math problem, the 3-Act Math® task roots the learner in the math problem through visualization of the actual real-world problem.

self. Fortunately, there are educators out there who have put together spreadsheets with 3-Act lessons you can use for free. Go to classroomchef.com/links and scroll down. You'll find plenty of lessons for almost any topic you need.

Step 2: Vet the Content

One massive mistake I made early in my teaching career was trusting the content I'd just obtained from another source. I downloaded a lesson that had a great title and matched exactly what I'd be teaching the next day, and assumed the author's work would be precisely what my students would need. Too often it wasn't. The video was not what I needed and didn't explain things in the way my students were used to hearing it. The lesson tanked. Even though the people who created the content have a great reputation, what they present may not be exactly what you need for your kids, so make sure all materials are just right before going in!

Step 3: Give Yourself Time

Yes, 3-Act tasks will take longer than a traditional lecture, but the time spent is valuable and necessary for students to really understand a concept. If you are going to paint a house, you can go quickly, covering as much area as possible with as little paint as possible. But when you want to paint a picture to be framed for everyone to enjoy, you take your time. Find different ways to represent an idea and let your creativity roam.

3-Act tasks will take more time, but the net gains in student curiosity are worth the extra minutes.

Key Points to Remember:

- Be willing to take a risk.
- Let students get curious. (Avoid supplying them with the solution too soon.)
- Give ample time.

- Use the free lessons until you get comfortable with the format and start generating more ideas of your own.
- These lessons are designed to invite a struggle; let students struggle.

Adaptations for Primary Students:

- Some of the contributors to classroomchef.com are elementary teachers, so you can easily find tasks for whatever grade level you teach. After having numerous conversations with Graham Fletcher, author of gfletchy.com and 3-Act Math activities, it has become evident to us that every child at every level wants to explore curiosities that these tasks provide. In *The Classroom Chef*, Jamie Duncan shares a lesson she did with her first graders involving Oreos. The conversations that her students were having, the ideas they came up with, and the mathematics that naturally rose to the top were phenomenal.
- If you're going to create your own lessons for littles, you know your kids and how big of a risk they are willing to take. Once you've used others' content and feel comfortable with the model, we look forward to hearing about the tasks you have created.

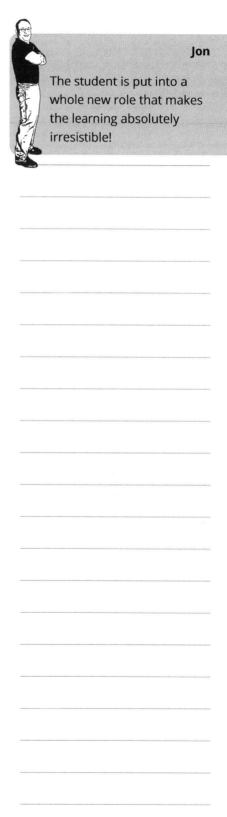

Jon

The student is put into a whole new role that makes the learning absolutely irresistible!

Chapter 11
Learning in the Round EduProtocol

Imagine a classroom where all the students are up at the **board with partners working on math problems.** Soft music plays in the background, and there is a relaxed but intentional hum in the room. The teacher is circling the room, scanning the boards. "Good work there." "Yes, that is correct." "Check your math right here." Students lean into their partners and talk softly, pointing here and there adjusting their work. Students are smiling and they appear to be feeling good about learning math today. This is what a Learning in the Round classroom looks like.

Academic Goals:

- Understand steps to solve problems.
- Discuss the work of peers using academic vocabulary.
- Work collaboratively and individually.

Math Practices:

- CCSS MATH PRACTICE: MP1: Make sense of problems and persevere in solving them.
- CCSS MATH PRACTICE: MP2: Reason abstractly and quantitatively.
- CCSS MATH PRACTICE: MP3: Construct viable arguments and critique the reasoning of others.
- CCSS MATH PRACTICE: MP5: Use appropriate tools strategically.
- CCSS MATH PRACTICE: MP6: Attend to precision.
- CCSS MATH PRACTICE: MP7: Look for and make use of structure.

Teacher Big Ideas:

- Checking for understanding is easy because student work visibility is maximized.
- Persevere, communicate, collaborate, and ask more questions in a fun and low-risk learning environment.
- Share their thinking and different strategies because there is no "front of the room."

Description:

In this protocol, students become the performers in the classroom and take an active role in understanding concepts by collaborating with their peers on whiteboard surfaces. The teacher stands at the center of the classroom and can easily check for understanding, provide reteaching, or ask guiding questions to large groups of students at a time. The Learning in the Round format can be applied to a variety of subjects: ELA, science, history, and math in all grade levels. Some of the inspiration for Learning in the Round came from Tim Bedley's Gallery Learning. For more information about getting kids up and working on whiteboards in the classroom, visit Tim's website at sites.google.com/site/gallerylearning1. Sean Kavanaugh was also a pioneer in learning using whiteboards to retool how math was taught, and was featured in the documentary *Teach*. More information can be found at 360degreemath.com.

Students Learning in the Round

Prepare for the Activity:

Ed Campos Jr., former math and computer science teacher now working with the Bootstrap program, describes how he prepares the Learning in the Round environment to get kids up and engaged:

Maximize the number of whiteboards placed around the classroom walls so every student can have their own individual workspace. Although students will work in pairs much of the time, it's important for each student to have a whiteboard section because they may need more think time to work problems out on their own before they share with a partner.

You can also start with an inexpensive alternative such as dry-erase sheets instead of permanent boards mounted on the walls. Some teachers tape off sections for each student workspace. In order to maximize the whiteboard space on the walls, it's important to adopt a minimalist attitude when it comes to the amount of clutter in the classroom and on the walls. Use a well-defined system to assign student pairs to work together. Some teachers use a deck of cards or a random name picker. As a bonus, add some music and music cues to the mix. Queue up a playlist that you can play in the background while students work.

Instructions:

Put a rich, open task up on the projector and have students partner up to work together on the problem. Here are some great resources for rich, open, and visual math tasks: visualpatterns.org, youcubed.org, and openmiddle.com.

You can use a music cue to signal that it's time to get up and work on the whiteboards. I use "Get Up, Stand Up" by Bob Marley. Allow time for the students to collaborate and work through different strategies while the teacher stands in the middle or walks around closer to the walls and asks guiding questions. Use a laser pointer to highlight student work or address misconceptions and mistakes.

When you feel that most students have completed the task, have them stop working and look at their classmates' work to compare and contrast the thinking and strategies. I've done this by asking them to move two whiteboards to the left (while Beyoncé's "To the Left, to the Left" plays) to analyze that pair's work.

After some time, have them gallery-walk around the room to see the different approaches before arriving back at their workstation (I'll play Run-DMC's "Walk This Way" or the Bangles' "Walk Like an Egyptian" during the gallery walk). Lastly, the teacher stands in the middle of the classroom while randomly calling on students to share out their answers and strategies.

Key Points to Remember:

- Choosing a rich, open, and preferably visual task is key, especially in math. You can document student work with your cell phone or iPad and project examples on your whiteboard to discuss.

- It's crucial to allow students to see other student work via a gallery walk before sharing out their solutions.

- When students are sharing out strategies, it's important to highlight how several different strategies can arrive at the same answer.

- Switching up the partners often is key to creating a culture where your students expect to work with different people every day.

Adaptations for Primary Students:

Primary students can use whiteboards in the classroom as well. Just get them up and engaged at the board. Start slowly. Follow pair sharing with a time for students to share out their process and thinking with the whole class.

SECTION 3
A Guide to New EduProtocols

Chapter 12
The Visual Directions EduProtocol

"What hat are we supposed to be doing?" said Max for the fourth time since class started three minutes ago, immediately following both oral and projected directions.** As teachers, we seem to have at least one Max in every class, and with up to seven periods a day that can be a lot of repeated directions. The Visual Directions EduProtocol was developed to address this constant classroom challenge by using familiar images to create visual directions for students. These visual directions typically use icons and are easier to comprehend quickly than print directions for our English language learners and students with learning challenges at all grade levels. The goal is that in lieu of the teacher giving the students directions, the students are responsible for telling the teacher what they are going to be doing. That is, the teacher shares the visual directions and asks the students to explain what it is they will be doing in this task. The roles are reversed, students are making their own connections with the directions, and now Max can own his learning!

Academic Goals:

- Clarifying the conveyance of directions.
- Seeking input from learners to tell you their understanding of directions.
- Visually telling directions in a few icons, makes clear what is essential to task.

Teacher Big Ideas:

- One of the most difficult and tiresome parts of working with dozens to hundreds of kids is having to repeat directions multiple times.

- This process seeks to invite the students into the mix, to collaborate, to interpret and make sense of visual cues, and to take a risk in sharing their interpretation with a partner or whole class.
- Most importantly, it provides a pathway for students to make sense of what they are going to be doing from their peers and their own voices.

Description:

Jeremiah's mentor, Phil White, always shared the following advice: "Never tell a student something they can tell you . . ." Phil's wise words led Jeremiah to the construction of a non-verbal way to elicit student understanding through their own feedback. Students are shown a series of images describing the directions to their next task, followed by the prompt.

This thought process, over time, led to the idea that if directions could be projected for the task students were going to engage in as a series of icons, the teacher could then say, "Your directions are on the next slide. With your partner, determine what you are going to be doing." The teacher shows students the slide, provides some think time, lets students discuss, and monitors their conversations. When the buzz of their conversations dies down, the teacher would then either select a few students to share out or elicit volunteer responses. That hard wait time for students to respond is critical here (especially the first couple of times we do this in class), as it is scary to take a risk on being wrong in this abstract way. Once that inertia is broken, there is a typical increasing volume of input as the wave of understanding crashes upon our shores and washes away the confusion and doubt. After their input is connected, just walk through the steps incorporating students' language and clarifying things that may not have been clear or were not addressed.

Here's an example: take a look at the image of a typical slide that Jeremiah often uses with kindergarten through eighth grade.

When I show students this I get a lot of responses about the eyes, and eventually some about the word "me." I respond, "How might the eyes and the use of the word 'me' be related?" The sea of puzzled looks is wiped away when I say this slide says, "Eyes on me," and then I ask, "What do you think that means?" My favorite response came from a first grader who said, "It means we stop squawking and look at you." I know, right?! I continue with, "That's right; this is my call for the whole class's attention." After we practice this a few times, being silly of course helps make this really sticky, but that's just a personal preference.

Next we get into the instructions of a task or the lesson. I share another example below, but try not to jump down below the picture. See if you can figure out what the directions are for the students.

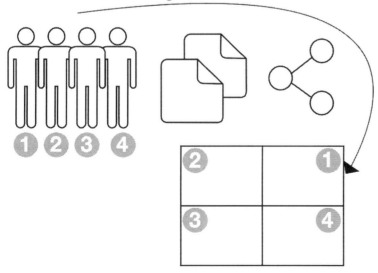

We would go through a similar routine as described above, and then I fill in whatever the students didn't get. Typically, my summary would be something like, "Yes, we'll be in groups of four, you will number off 1 through 4, each person will receive two sheets of paper, and each person will share their results with the group. If you are Number 3, then your job is to complete the task in Quadrant 3 for your group and, when directed, share your learning with your group. Everyone with their number on their finger, hold them high . . . okay, with your other hand point at your quadrant. Okay, you may begin."

If you're wondering how much time this takes, you'll be surprised to know that most first repetitions with this are less than five minutes, even in kindergarten, and it only gets faster from there. By the end of the first month of school, my kids could go through the routine in about two minutes with sharing out. Eventually, I just had to place the icons up and kids already knew what they meant. In short succession, this process actually saves you time because everyone is clear on their directions—even English language learners and students with special needs. When someone forgets, they are able to ask their partner or refer to the icons again as a quick, nonverbal reminder. And, because the kids feel like they are telling you, there is very little pushback on jumping into the learning. We, as humans, rarely like to be told what to do, but we don't mind sharing what we will be doing.

Prepare for the Activity:

Step 1: Clarify your directions to no more than six or seven steps—usually three or four is a good number.

Step 2: Determine what word, action, or idea is most important in each step.

Step 3: Think of an icon or image that captures the essence you determined in Step 2.

Step 4: Create the images, use the Google Add-on "Insert Icons for Slides," obtain from the Noun Project, purchase the images, or use Creative Commons–licensed images to create your masterpiece.

Step 5: Ensure that the order of the steps flows with how you are displaying them on the slide.

Instructions:

Step 1: In the learning environment, make sure everyone has a partner before showing the slide. Make sure you know how you would like students to share their learning when you come back together, and share this with them in the next step.

Step 2: Tell the learners, "On the next slide are the directions for what you will be doing for the next few minutes. With your partner, determine what those directions might be. When we all come back together, I will have you share out by . . ."

Step 3: Show the learners your created slide, walk around the room, and listen to the students' conversations. See if you can pick up what is standing out to them and what is still unclear.

Step 4: When conversations begin to slow down, bring everyone back together and have them share out in the process you described earlier. Allow two to four student groups to share, and then use their responses and fill in any missing directions.

Useful Symbols

Share

Slides or Power Point

Repeat 3 times

On your computer

Two slides

Number of people in a group with designated slides for each

Paper

Key Points to Remember:

- You may select and sequence the responses of students if you hear something you'd like to share or to change up the variety of responses.

- In Step 4, it is beneficial to point at each icon (or image) as you describe what they are going to be doing throughout the process.

- Often the first couple of times you do this, or with new direction sets, there is going to be confusion and misunderstanding. Anticipate that. Pro tip: see if you can test-drive your new slide of directions with people in your life that can give you honest feedback, and make the appropriate adjustments.

- The wait time is important; overcoming the inertia of not responding because of the novelty of the act and the fear of being wrong may be surprising at first, but it pays off once the responses start pouring in.

Adaptations for Primary Students:

Like in the "Eyes on Me" example shown above, the slides should be appropriate for primary students to access and understand. Keep the amount of content to one slide per direction and keep it as simple as you can. All learners love it if you can be a little silly with this, like asking silly questions, changing your voice, or having them practice; little kids especially love this. Don't underestimate what kids can give you when given the chance, just be sure to keep it to one slide per step and they'll be right there with you.

Pro Tip: Label each icon with a descriptive filename and store them all in one place in Drive. Jeremiah keeps his in a folder called ICONS so they're easy to find and use.

There is no end to the variations that can be created when playing tic-tac-toe. This Math EduProtocol allows the teacher to direct the students' focus to particular skill sets and allows students to work together in a familiar and friendly way. In one version, each tile or square has a particular skill to be practiced (addition, subtraction, etc.). In another version a teacher may choose to create a game board for the students with predetermined problems. This allows teachers to design a game board that has carefully placed Depth of Knowledge (DOK) questions. The genius behind this EduProtocol is that no matter who chooses the square, both students are working on the problem independently and comparing answers. This allows students to be precise, think critically, construct logical arguments, and critique others' thinking.

Academic Goals:

- Review math concepts in a fun manner.
- Analyze and critique the reasoning of others.
- Discuss what is understood and what isn't.

Math Practices:

- CCSS MATH PRACTICE: MP3: Construct viable arguments and critique the reasoning of others.
- CCSS MATH PRACTICE: MP5: Use appropriate tools strategically.
- CCSS MATH PRACTICE: MP6: Attend to precision.

Teacher Big Ideas:

- Most students know how to play the x's and o's version of tic-tac-toe. Therefore, the learning curve is shortened, allowing students and teachers to focus on the task of review.
- It is a low-prep activity that can be enjoyed during any part of a unit.
- All students are engaged at all times whether it's their turn or not.

Description:

This basic version has squares with a predetermined function to solve. For example, in the four corners, students add digits (1, 2, 3, or more depending on standards) to find the sum. Students subtract the numbers in the outside middle squares. The center square is for a multiplication problem. In another version, students answer math questions that increase in DOK difficulty, racing to be the first to answer three in a row. This math twist to an old favorite makes reviewing math fun and engaging. The Four Cs focus of this EduProtocol is collaboration and critical thinking.

The RSP teacher at Lisa's school is tickled pink with this protocol: "I am a resource teacher, grades K–5. I liked the idea of the Depth of Knowledge within the [tic-tac-toe] game, as well as the adaptability within the game. We use playing cards for math warm-ups. The cards allow us to create random numbers (pending which card comes up next) to practice basic calculation skills." (Tressa Luke, Resource Specialist, King City Arts Magnet School)

Prepare for the Activity:

Step 1: Prepare a tic-tac-toe board (digital, paper, or on a whiteboard) for students to use.

Step 2: Share the tasks that students will complete in each square.

Step 3: Have students use number tiles or a deck of cards (minus the face cards and 10).

Heather Politi has created a digital tic-tac-toe board:
bit.ly/tic-tac-toe-ep

Lisa

I had been on a roll, taking familiar games and ideas and making them relatable to math. I'm obsessed with repurposing everyday things for math education. My brain simply works differently. I see an idea, be it language arts–related or a game, and I can't help but think, "Oh, that can so easily be in a math class." Apparently, it's a gift. I've talked to others who have created amazing classroom tools, and their response? "Really? I'd love to hear about it."

Jon

Learning gains traction when it is fun!

Instructions:

Step 1: Have students pair up.

Step 2: Give each pair number tiles or a deck of cards.

Step 3: Predetermine what function the students will complete in each square.

Step 4: Give students a tic-tac-toe board, using a digital copy, paper, or whiteboard.

Step 5: Student A draws as many cards as needed to create a problem. If your students are practicing numbers to one thousand (second-grade standard), you may want students to choose six cards to create two three-digit numbers to add or subtract.

Step 6: Both Student A and Student B independently solve the equation. When both have solved the equation, Students A and B compare answers. If Student A is correct, Student A gets the square. If Student A is incorrect and Student B is correct, Student B can steal the square from Student A.

Step 7: Students alternate turns until someone wins or the board is completed.

Variations:

VERSION 1: Create a board using only algorithms. If students are working on specific algorithms such as multiplying whole numbers or adding fractions, you can create a board that targets areas the class might be having difficulty with. For example, multiplying fractions using the algorithm where a zero is in the ones place (for example, 360 x 23) can be tricky for students. Having a game board in which each of the nine squares features this allows students nine repetitions.

VERSION 2: Have both students work on the center square together, and both claim it. Since the most coveted and challenging spot is the center square, students may want to work on it together. Working on it together allows for true collaboration and discussion about processes. It will enable students to learn from one another.

Marlena

Claiming the middle square by both students was an idea that came from students. We loved how they decided that they could work together and share the glory of success.

VERSION 3: Have students work in teams. Sometimes pairing students together in teams allows for deeper understanding and a greater sense of success.

Tick-Tack-Toe Board Layout for DOK Version

DOK 1	DOK 2	DOK 1
DOK 2	DOK 2 or DOK 3	DOK 2
DOK 1	DOK 2	DOK 1

This DOK version is set up similar to the previous version with the addition of Webb's DOK. In this version, the teacher chooses between one and three standards on which to focus. The four corners have problems that are a DOK 1.

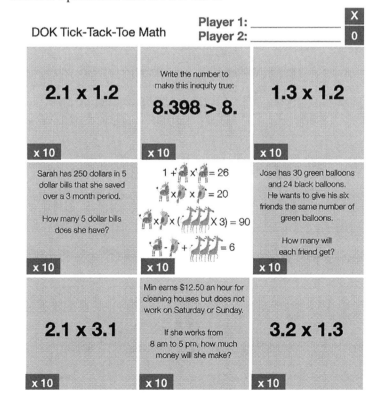

DOK Tick-Tack-Toe Math

Player 1: _____

Player 2: _____

X

0

2.1×1.2 x 10	Write the number to make this inequity true: $8.398 > 8.$ x 10	1.3×1.2 x 10
Sarah has 250 dollars in 5 dollar bills that she saved over a 3 month period. How many 5 dollar bills does she have? x 10	$1 + \text{🐫} \times \text{🐫} = 26$ $\text{🐫} \times \text{🐪} \times \text{🐪} = 20$ $\text{🐫} \times \text{🐪} \times (\text{🦙} \times 3) = 90$ $\text{🐫} - \text{🐪} + \text{🦙} = 6$ x 10	Jose has 30 green balloons and 24 black balloons. He wants to give his six friends the same number of green balloons. How many will each friend get? x 10
2.1×3.1 x 10	Min earns $12.50 an hour for cleaning houses but does not work on Saturday or Sunday. If she works from 8 am to 5 pm, how much money will she make? x 10	3.2×1.3 x 10

The outside center squares contain DOK 2 problems, whereas the center square is the most difficult with a rigorous DOK 2 or DOK 3 problem. Have both players work on the center square collaboratively. Then they can *both* claim the square.

Use this chart to help you apply the DOK level prompts to the mathematics questions you develop.

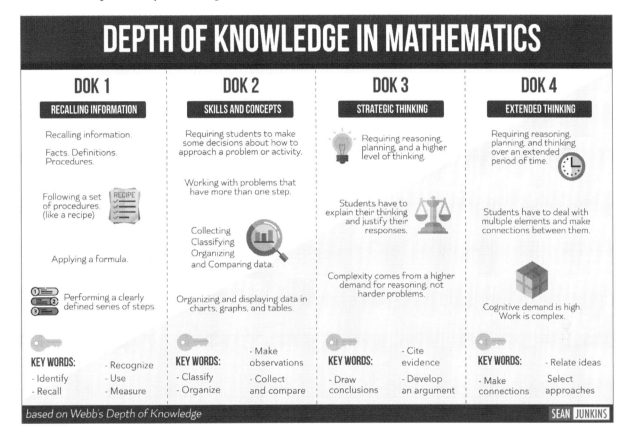

DEPTH OF KNOWLEDGE IN MATHEMATICS

DOK 1	DOK 2	DOK 3	DOK 4
RECALLING INFORMATION	SKILLS AND CONCEPTS	STRATEGIC THINKING	EXTENDED THINKING
Recalling information.	Requiring students to make some decisions about how to approach a problem or activity.	Requiring reasoning, planning, and a higher level of thinking.	Requiring reasoning, planning, and thinking over an extended period of time.
Facts. Definitions. Procedures.			
Following a set of procedures. (like a recipe)	Working with problems that have more than one step.	Students have to explain their thinking and justify their responses.	Students have to deal with multiple elements and make connections between them.
Applying a formula.	Collecting Classifying Organizing and Comparing data.		
Performing a clearly defined series of steps.	Organizing and displaying data in charts, graphs, and tables.	Complexity comes from a higher demand for reasoning, not harder problems.	Cognitive demand is high. Work is complex.
KEY WORDS: - Identify - Recall - Recognize - Use - Measure	**KEY WORDS:** - Classify - Organize - Make observations - Collect and compare	**KEY WORDS:** - Draw conclusions - Cite evidence - Develop an argument	**KEY WORDS:** - Make connections - Relate ideas Select approaches

based on Webb's Depth of Knowledge   SEAN JUNKINS

Key Points to Remember:

- Working in partners, students will independently solve the problems on the tic-tac-toe board, allowing students time to analyze each other's work.
- The goal is to have both students work on the same problem independently in order to compare, defend, and discuss their work.
- Tic-tac-toe makes a fun review for students.
- Have both players work on the center square collaboratively. Then they can *both* claim the square.

- Use this as an end of unit/concept review.
- Choose two to three standards on which to focus.
- The center square should review the most challenging task.
- This is supposed to be a fun game; keep the atmosphere in your classroom fun but focused.

Jeremiah

Having students create their own problems is fun, especially when they see it on the next iteration of this EduProtocol.

Tick-Tack-Toe

Add two 2-digit numbers: (example) 45 + 13	Add two 3-digit numbers (example) 745 + 437	Add two 2-digit numbers:
Add two 3-digit numbers	Subtract two 3-digit numbers (example) 472 - 237	Add two 3-digit numbers
Add two 2-digit numbers:	Add 2 3-digit numbers	Add two 2-digit numbers:

Adaptations for Primary Students:

To ensure that all students understand how tic-tac-toe is played, you may want to play a traditional game using x's and o's in the boxes. Once students understand this, they can begin playing the game.

It may be helpful for students to see how the game is played with math problems in the boxes. This can easily be accomplished by having whole group games. In one version students can play against the teacher. In another, half the class can play against the other half. Once students understand how to play, they should be able to play this simple but fun game on their own. Consider moving the game into centers or independent practice once students understand the rules.

The Chatterbox EduProtocol

The purpose of this gamified EduProtocol is to encourage students to discuss keywords, concepts, or operations in a fun and agile environment. Give students multiple chances for making sense of the many big ideas in mathematics while providing an exciting, interactive process for all to enjoy. Modeled after the 1960s television show *Password*, the concept for this protocol was originally published in *Building Academic Vocabulary* by Robert Marzano and Debra Pickering.

Jeremiah

We recommend checking out Steve Wyborney's blog for his interpretation of TAMAM (Talk a Mile a Minute).

Academic Goals:

- Students discuss and practice using keywords and vocabulary in a fun, engaging way.
- Students grapple with how mathematical ideas relate.
- Embedded review as directed by the teacher or needed by students.

Math Practices:

- CCSS MATH PRACTICE: MP1: Make sense of problems and persevere in solving them.
- CCSS MATH PRACTICE: MP3: Construct viable arguments and critique the reasoning of others.
- CCSS MATH PRACTICE: MP7: Look for and make use of structure.

Teacher Big Ideas:

- Students interact with keywords or concepts through preview, review, or formative assessment.
- Students engage in utilizing language to make sense of mathematics.
- Students consider relationships between concepts.

Description:

Several words under a common category are chosen and displayed on a slide in the front of the room. In pairs, students explain the concept or topic displayed. One partner has their back to the slide, leaving the view and the explanation to the other partner. The student with their back to the slide listens and tries to guess what is on the slide from their partner's explanation and description. This listening/talking partnership is designed to develop a concept, visualization skills, and listening skills. After one minute, both partners view the words and discuss them. The whole class then tries to figure out the category.

Jeremiah

Having students talk and discuss is an integral part of their learning process. Many times, teachers struggle to find meaningful talk in their classrooms. This is a great way to integrate other standards such as ELD, speaking, and listening.

One partner faces the board so they can see the word; the other partner has their back to the board as they try to guess the word based on the clues their partner gives.

Prepare for the Activity:

Step 1: Utilizing a slide deck template, determine what key ideas are most important for utilizing Chatterbox. Key ideas, pictures, or concepts could be a single word, word phrases, or images grouped in a meaningful way. Groups of keywords should be placed as a list on a single slide, with one theme or domain as a commonality between all selected words or ideas, images, or word phrases.

Step 2: After preparing each slide as described above, scaffold the intentional reveal of the items to develop student understanding of the central concept.

Step 3: The timer on each slide should be set for one minute.

Step 4: Ensure a balance of content slides and fun slides. Also, ensure content varies so that all players have opportunities to access the material. This balance provides that necessary brain break between heavy content and will pique students' interest in what will be on the next slide. The success of this protocol hinges on a proper balance and a random mix of both fun slides and content slides.

Step 5: After completing each round, highlight the two to four slides per round of seven slides you would like to review. Further discussion is a powerful opportunity to strengthen connections and tie into the common category showcased on the individual slides.

Instructions:

Step 1: While pairs of students will be facing each other, one partner will have their back to the display screen and the other will be facing the display screen.

Step 2: The student facing the screen may use any words to describe the word, phrase, or picture, but cannot say the word itself, any part of the word, or things like, "it rhymes with . . .", "it sounds like . . .", "it starts with the letter . . .", etc. The student trying to guess may skip words or phrases during the one-minute episode.

Step 3: Keeping score is up to the teacher and students to decide, or simply by asking how many were able to get so many words, etc. The goal is to have positive interactions and the opportunity for conversation that will flow from this experience.

Step 4: Once the one minute has elapsed, have partners discuss.

Step 5: The whole class discusses the possible category to which the descriptors on the page connect before the teacher reveals the answer.

Step 6: As a bonus, the teacher may highlight two to four of the categories and words to have students review and discuss at the end of the seven rounds. While seven rounds are not a required number of rounds, it tends to be the "just right" amount of time to keep the experience moving forward.

Key Points to Remember:

- If the balance isn't maintained between content and fun slides, the learning and momentum will come to a grinding halt. Keep in mind that if seven rounds are the typical amount, three or four slides should be universally accessible to the entire audience.

- To cover more content, institute two or three iterations of the seven rounds over a couple of days. Students won't mind because they are interacting positively with their construction of learning.

- Be comfortable with students describing words or phrases using non-academic language, or completely unrelated descriptions; this makes the learning sticky and is a powerful connection to bring between the teacher and student.

Adaptations for Primary Students:

- Use familiar images and graphics for students to describe. Consider using simple math problems.
- Keep time shorter, say twenty seconds.
- Build up to longer times as the year progresses.

Jeremiah

I have used this at all levels from kinder to adult learners, and it is always a highlight. Remember the fun in this EduProtocol comes in providing opportunities for all learners, so balance the amount of content with non-content word groupings. Also remember to alternate who gets to say the nonacademic words and who is guessing them. If Partner A got to guess the nonacademic words, then their next turn they should have to describe the nonacademic words.

- Provide scaffolds for language and class discussion as needed, such as sentence frames, to get students started. Sentence frames are also beneficial for English language learners.

Chapter 15
Number Stories EduProtocol

In this creative and open-ended EduProtocol, young students manipulate digital characters of themselves and their classmates to create, retell, and write math stories.

About the Creators:

Christine Pinto and Jessica Twomey are early childhood educators whose classes have been collaborating daily from their locations in California and New Jersey for several years and are coauthors of *Innovating Play*. You can connect with them on Twitter @PintoBeanz11 and @jlabar2me, or on their website at innovatingplay .world.

Academic Goals:

- Integrate reading, writing, and math content.
- To build number sense in young children as they begin to explore addition and subtraction.
- To allow young children to socialize and engage in play through learning.

Math Practices:

- CCSS MATH PRACTICE: MP1: Make sense of problems and persevere in solving them.
- CCSS MATH PRACTICE: MP2: Reason abstractly and quantitatively.
- CCSS MATH PRACTICE: MP4: Model with mathematics.

Teacher Big Ideas:

- Development of mathematical thinking in young children happens in three critical stages: concrete, pictorial, and abstract. To develop a firm foundation in mathematics, children must have the opportunity to manipulate objects (concrete), show their thinking in pictures (pictorial), and finally, represent their ideas in mathematical symbols (abstract).

- Connecting mathematical thinking to children's natural play patterns and experiences supports engagement and depth of understanding.

- Throughout this four-week study, embrace the opportunity to incorporate reading, writing, speaking, listening, and viewing to create and solve number stories in all three stages of development.

Description:

This EduProtocol is adapted from Christine and Jessica's Creative Play activity Number Stories from *Innovating Play*, in which joyful, life-long thinkers and learners are fostered and supported. Students use character blocks to act out and record stories focused on addition and subtraction.

For more information on the Number Stories Study, where children explore playful centers to build connections on the various math and language components to number stories, visit innovatingplay.world.

Marlena
We love this protocol because of its natural interdisciplinary nature.

Prepare for the Activity:

Prepare slides for student work. Add images of characters students are reading about or images of students to the side of a slide. Add a background to the slide, such as a playground or other scene with which students are familiar. (Students will drag and drop the images they choose onto the background.)

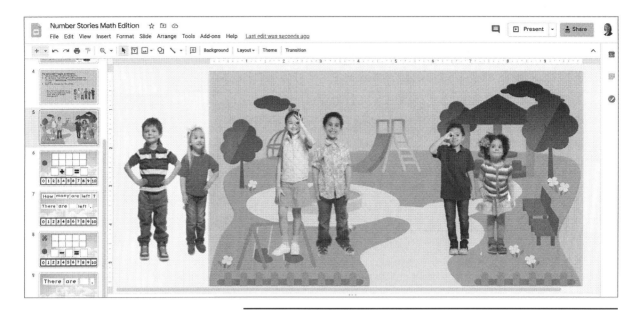

Template: *Get the Number Stories Math EduProtocol template at bit.ly/number-stories-math*

Instructions:

Step 1: Students manipulate the characters on the slide as they create their number stories. Students record the story on the following slides. Access a template at bit.ly/number-stories-eduprotocol

Step 2: Students record the story that they created into their paper book. Find a sample at innovatingplay.world/numberstoriesbook.

Step 3: Students share the slides that they created so that other students can solve the stories.

Variations:

VERSION 1: As a culminating experience, use a Number Story Flipgrid to assess student understanding. This allows children an authentic audience to publish to, communicate with, and support learning through collaboration. Each child may have the opportunity to read and act out their story with their personalized people. Extend by recording each student, allowing for individualized guidance, and checking for understanding.

VERSION 2: After all the number stories are recorded children may use the Number Story Flipgrid on Chromebooks, along with paper-and-pencil recording sheets, to solve number stories created by their peers.

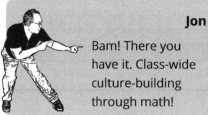

Jon

Bam! There you have it. Class-wide culture-building through math!

Student recording his story in a Number Story book.

Key Points to Remember:

- Rich play-based experiences require time and thoughtful preparation. Children will make deeper connections to academic content when they are both engaged and invested in their experiences.
- Recording an entire class of Number Stories individually in kindergarten will not be perfect! Accept and value the process of learning together.
- Allowing children to be creators and teachers for each other gives value to their voice and their process as active contributors in the learning process.

Pro Tip: Remove the background from the images of students easily with a program such as remove.bg.

Chapter 16
Comic Strip Math EduProtocol

Finding opportunities to allow students to slow their think-ing down so that they can explain their thought process can be challenging. This EduProtocol forces students to explain each step in a fun and engaging manner. The Mathemagicalville comic gives students the scaffold needed to make their thinking transparent by explaining themselves, all while using a comic-style template that can be made into a comic book of learning at the end. This Math EduProtocol allows students to be thoughtful, explicit, and creative. It allows teachers to home in on student understanding and, in some cases, misunderstandings. The teacher may choose to collect the students' work over the course of a unit, marking period, or year to create a math comic book as a record of learning.

Academic Goals:

- Give students the tools necessary to understand a problem and create a plan.
- Help students to break apart a problem.
- Dialogue and write steps for solving.

Math Practices:

- CCSS MATH PRACTICE: MP1: Make sense of problems and persevere in solving them.
- CCSS MATH PRACTICE: MP2: Reason abstractly and quantitatively.

Teacher Big Ideas:

- Allow student space to stop, think out, and explain their thought process for solving a math problem.

- This is not a daily protocol.
- This protocol may be used to enhance the assessment process of MathReps. After four days of doing a daily MathRep, take one particular problem that focused on a specific skill set and use Comic Strip Math to expand and make visible a student's thought process.
- Slow math down through writing so that weaknesses or misconceptions become apparent.

Description:

In this Math EduProtocol students focus on breaking down one problem into steps in a fun way. The teacher gives the students a problem to solve. Not only do the students need to show their work, they also need to explain their thinking. Doing so as a comic allows students to have fun, show off their creative skills, and express their thinking in a less rigid manner. This EduProtocol can be used throughout the year and kept in order to create a unique comic book where the hero defeats the villain.

Prepare for the Activity:

Prepare Mathemagicalville Comic for each student, either digitally or on paper. When using a word problem, type the information in the speech bubble (first square) then pass out to students. In Step 1, Step 2, and Step 3, there is a small cloud in the corner where the teacher can put hints to help students along. Find the template here: bit.ly/ComicStripMath.

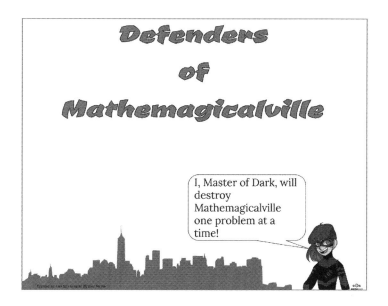

Jeremiah

The interdisciplinary angle is so great here, and kids love to make their stories fun. I have had success with my middle schoolers building the Comic Strip around class and school events, such as dances and spirit week.

Lisa

The versatility of this EduProtocol makes it easy to incorporate into almost any classroom. Teachers can choose to give hints or not. Students have the freedom to be creative in ways that they may not have been before. From my experience, students may start off timid in the creativity department with this activity but soon embrace it, truly taking ownership over their learning.

Instructions:

Step 1: Students will begin at Step 1 on the template, writing their thoughts in the top rectangular space marked "Step 1."

Step 2: Students will show their work in the larger rectangular box below Step 1. There is also space for them to draw themselves as the superhero.

Step 3: Students will repeat this process with Step 2 and Step 3 on the template, where they finally solve the problem and defeat the villain.

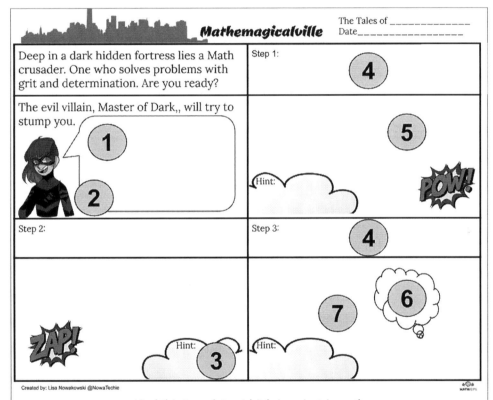

Find this template at bit.ly/comicstripmath

1. Write the problem the students will solve here! Adding a message from the villain is a fun twist.

2. The villain, Master of Dark, was designed as a gender-neutral character.

3. Teachers may choose to give a hint to help guide students in any step.

4. Students write what they will do here for each frame.

5. Students will work out the first step in this space.

6. The students write a victory message about defeating Master of Dark.

7. Students draw their comic selves here.

Key Points to Remember:

- Students enjoy this protocol because they are active participants in the imagination of the solution.
- Keep it fun but keep it real.
- Older students (8–12) can still use this format and flow without the comic book characters (but a little fun doesn't hurt!).

Variations:

VERSION 1: Change the name and use as a STEM/STEAM activity. Present students with a problem where the villain challenges our hero. Each box shows either the steps they would use to solve the problem *or* the iterations the students went through to solve the problem, with the last box being the final iteration, thus defeating Master of Dark.

VERSION 2: Keep student work and compile it into a comic book for them to take home at the end of the year, marking period, or math domain.

Adaptations for Primary Students:

Teachers can place sentence frames in the boxes to help students get started and on the right track. Alternatively, sentence stems may be placed on paper sentence strips for students to copy. Throughout the year, the teacher should scale back the scaffolding in order to create independent thinkers/learners.

Lisa

If you have an idea for a new EduProtocol, try it out with your students. Then, invite them to help you make it better. Not only will you have a better product, but the students will be invested and engaged. It's quite an experience to collaborate with your students no matter the age level.

Chapter 17
Write Bytes EduProtocol

Write Bytes allows students to view a situation or image through various lenses. As in real life, there is often more than one way to view a situation and find an accurate solution. This EduProtocol challenges students to produce four equations based on an image. Write Bytes further stretches the students' understanding by having them create a word problem that relates to one of the equations previously generated.

Academic Goals:

- To help build number sense in students.
- To facilitate deeper thinking about numbers.
- To help students see equations in real world situations (word problems).

Math Practices:

- CCSS MATH PRACTICE: MP3: Construct viable arguments and critique the reasoning of others.
- CCSS MATH PRACTICE: MP7: Look for and make use of structure.

Teacher Big Ideas:

- Students will plan, revise, and look for patterns. They will understand what they are looking at and make meaning out of the image.
- Students find different ways to break the image apart, manipulate it, and represent what they see.
- Students write a word problem that relates to one of their equations.

Description:

Write Bytes are short (ten minutes or less) talks with students to build number sense and connect images to symbols and numbers. These can work in any grade. Most often, the teacher leads the group discussion and records student thinking. Write Bytes can use equations, numbers, or pictures.

Take a grid of nine delicious donuts, for example.

Each student will see this image differently. Some may look at this image and see three groups of three (3 x 3), others may see 3 + 3 + 3, and still others may see 3 + 6 (three are bitten and six are whole). Once students see the equation in the image, they record it.

Prepare for the Activity:

Step 1: Find and project the desired image. The website ntimages.weebly.com/photos.html has a collection of images that work well for this protocol.

Step 2: Distribute the Write Bytes template (below) to students, either digitally or as paper copies.

Step 3: Prepare a few equations of your own in case students need prompting.

Lisa

The ability for students to think about numbers, images, and situations flexibly takes time. While students may have difficulty creating a situation that matches the pattern or equation, with practice they will become more skilled at seeing the different patterns.

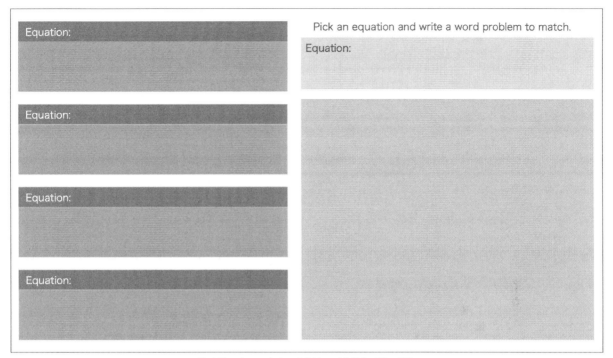

Get the template at https://bit.ly/3ba4Xjn

Instructions:

Step 1: Familiarize students with Write Bytes and your expectations.

Step 2: Distribute the recording sheet to students, either digitally or as hard copies.

Step 3: Project an image for students to analyze.

Step 4: Allow students time to think. We also encourage students to talk to one another to help spark new thoughts and ideas.

Step 5: Have students record their equations and their iterations of the equation as they think about it more and listen to their peers.

Step 6: In the large text box, each student chooses one equation that they will expand into a word problem. In the smaller box, on the right-hand side, they will write the equation they chose.

Jeremiah

The power of getting students to talk about math is so vital to their identity as a mathematician. Write Bytes is an empowering way to provide students a safe space to share their thinking, provided the environment is safe to explore and mistakes are valued.

Key Points to Remember:

- Students will need plenty of practice and exposure to oral-only class-wide Write Bytes before using this protocol.
- Students may create oral word stories to understand the images they see.
- Keep it quick; this is intended to be a ten-minute activity. If students don't finish all the writing, it's okay.

Adaptations for Primary Students:

- Instead of having students write a word problem, have them draw it!
- They will also enjoy recording and retelling their drawing in an app such as Seesaw or Flipgrid.

Chapter 18

Curiosity Creator EduProtocol

By our very nature human brains are wired to identify patterns and to resolve the unseen, which is why wrapped gifts seem so much more alluring than unwrapped gifts. Graphics are often presented in mathematics as unwrapped gifts that provide little opportunity for learners to grapple with and utilize our brains' hardwiring to make sense of the graphic.

Academic Goals:

- Make sense of graphics.
- Systematically attend to detail and precision .
- Foster universal access for learners.

Math Practices:

- CCSS MATH PRACTICE: MP1: Make sense of problems and persevere in solving them.
- CCSS MATH PRACTICE: MP6: Attend to precision.
- CCSS MATH PRACTICE: MP7: Look for and make use of structure.
- The Math Practices listed here for the Curiosity Creator are interlinked; they reinforce each other as the student makes sense of the graphic.

Teacher Big Ideas:

- Having students make sense of the graphic and attending to the details underscores the importance of this process.

- Since learners construct the meaning, the learner gains insight into the power of graphics and various ways of displaying information.
- Students build on previous knowledge to make sense of the graphics shown.

Description:

The Curiosity Creator highlights this idea by strategically hiding information and then helping learners go through a process to unveil the details one at a time and make sense of the graphics along the way.

Prepare for the Activity:

Step 1: The teacher finds a compelling graphic representation of the learning target(s) to utilize in the lesson. Some of the graphics have many hidden features to invite a discourse when viewed: few words, units, axis labels, descriptors, keywords in a chart title.

Each layer that is hidden will be systematically removed so that the full graphic will be revealed in time.

Step 2: Before each reveal, the teacher should ask a variety of strategic questions about the graphic to foster curiosity. As learners narrow their scope of vision to the intent of the graphics, the teacher should craft a series of questions that reveal key learning points about the graphics.

Step 3: The final reveal of information should help students construct the narrative that the graphics tell and should provide learners with a deep understanding of the key features of the graphics. Be sure that you know what this narrative might look like and guide students toward this narrative by asking questions while allowing students to come to varied conclusions.

Step 4: The teacher places the graphic in a slide deck. Hide all compelling information to be displayed to students with blocks covering some of the key details.

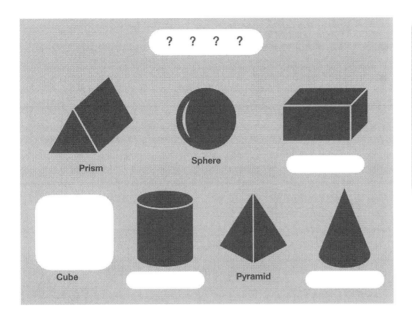

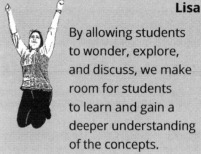

Instructions:

Step 1: Showcase the prepared graphic. Have students either mentally Notice and Wonder about the graphic, or provide a document for writing down their ideas. After students have had some individual think time, allow partners to share and revise their thinking.

Step 2: Once partners have shared and revised their thinking, provide space for a whole-class discussion. Once consensus of some ideas has taken shape, reveal the first level and repeat the process: students Notice and Wonder individually, then with partners, and then the whole class together.

Step 3: This process of noticing and wondering individually, then sharing with partners, and then the whole class after each reveal provides ample opportunities for students to make sense of the details the teacher has constructed for students to learn as well as supports our English language learners. In addition, the slow release process helps students learn to read graphics and make sense of the many details graphics often show but rarely illuminate for readers.

Jeremiah

This EduProtocol **works beautifully with any content area and for all grades!** Try it in science or social studies or ELA!

Using an online collection tool such as Socrative can allow learners to see others' thinking and provide teachers with data.

Step 4: The final process should reveal the original graphics, and the teacher should allow space for students to construct a narrative to describe their thinking about their learning from this process. For example, have students process their thinking in a quick write. They should reflect upon how their thinking changed from the initial view to the final view. Reflecting on what they noticed about the highlighted graphics is a powerful closure activity for this component of the lesson.

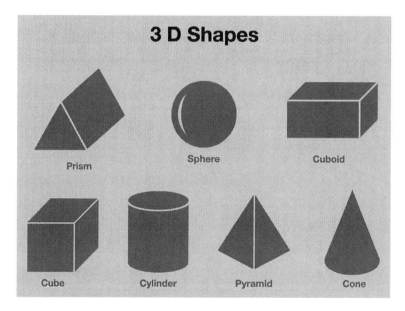

Key Points to Remember:

- The right graphic will make or break this protocol, so be sure the chosen graphics have enough interesting features to capture the audience's curiosity.
- Be sure to hide enough features that give away too much information; revealing too much information eliminates the curiosity element from the activity.
- Carefully select the sequence of the reveal with matching questions to guide students toward the desired learning goal.

Adaptations for Primary Students:

This is a fun activity with primary students, who are still full of learning curiosity!

- The graphics shown should be appropriate to the age and interest of the audience.
- Keep the interaction question simple to Notice and Wonder about the graphic.
- Plan the process so that it does not take too long, as young children have short attention spans.
- Utilize class-wide shared writing to summarize what they Noticed and Wondered between the original image and the final reveal.

Chapter 19
Convince Me That EduProtocol

Convince Me That is a protocol that gets students working toward communicating understanding rather than calculating solutions. By supplying students with the answer, their focus shifts toward creating a product that shows a greater depth of knowledge as they "convince us" that the solution is correct.

About the Creator:

Daniel Kaufmann is the K-12 Instructional Math Coach for the Wilson School District in West Lawn, PA. You can connect with Daniel on Twitter @KauDan721, or on his website at SCMath.org.

Academic Goals:

- Covers a wide range of math practices and standards.
- To become more comfortable in communicating mathematics.
- An understanding that being good at mathematics goes beyond the ability to produce answers.

Math Practices:

- CCSS MATH PRACTICE: MP2: Reason abstractly and quantitatively.
- CCSS MATH PRACTICE: MP5: Use appropriate tools strategically.
- CCSS MATH PRACTICE: MP7: Look for and make use of structure.

Teacher Big Ideas:

- This activity works because the fear of being wrong is alleviated by supplying the solution.
- Students engage in mathematics with a focus on communication, collaboration, creativity, and critical thinking.
- This activity can be easily applied to all topics of study and other subjects as well.
- When first starting this protocol, begin with one number and one equation for the students to write.

Description:

Pose a problem along with the solution. In pairs or small groups, students work to convince other groups and the teacher why the answer is correct. Encourage students to stay in the concrete and representational/pictorial stages of learning and not to jump to the abstract (typically an algorithm).

Prepare for the Activity:

Step 1: Identify a topic in which students have prior knowledge. The topic could be one that you are currently working on or a review.

Step 2: Create a digital slide to be projected for a problem to be solved. Replace the start of the problem (solve, graph, compare, etc.) with "Convince me that" and supply the answer. For example:

Compare 15.203 and 15.21 → Convince me that 15.203 is less than 15.21.

Instructions:

Step 1: Place students in pairs or small groups. This is a great opportunity to use random groups, as the students will only be working together for a short period of time (less than ten minutes).

Step 2: Limit their resources to one writing utensil and one piece of paper (or whiteboard) to help promote communication and collaboration. Also, limit the time that students can use to develop and present their arguments to help you maintain classroom structure and class flow.

Step 3: Reveal the problem and encourage students to work in the concrete and representational/pictorial stages. Jumping to the algorithm typically isn't convincing.

Step 4: Select which groups will share with the class.

Key Points to Remember:

- Spiral through previously learned concepts. Stick to the same concepts (exponents, factors, etc.) for a week, or more if necessary.

- Model, model, model! Don't jump into this EduProtocol too quickly as an independent protocol. Depending on the grade level, modeling as a class should occur for three to five days to be sure that students understand the expectations.

- Use sentence stems until students develop the academic vocabulary they need to effectively communicate their math ideas to one another.

Variations:

VERSION 1: Students work side-by-side with a partner to reflect on their problem-solving strategies. Give students a number or series of numbers. Split the paper into three sections. Section 1 is for Student A. Section 2 is where the numbers will be written, and section 3 is left for Student B.

Student A	Number	Student B

Jeremiah

I have been a huge fan of Convince Me That for years, and I love that you can keep this EduProtocol in your back pocket, so to speak, and pull it out whenever you want to generate a conversation or challenge a student's thinking. It is also a favorite way of mine to structure student discussion during a turn and talk.

Each student independently works on different ways to create the selected number. For example, if students will be working with the number 16, then both Student A and Student B find equations in which the answer will be 16. Each student will work independently on their equation before collaborating. The teacher should indicate specific parameters such as using three addends, using exponents, using multiplication and division, etc. However, it is essential to note that the students' equations can contain *more* than what is listed—and in fact, more is encouraged.

Example:

Student A	Number	Student B
$(3 \times 8) - 8$ $5 + (24 \div 2) - 1$	16 (Using x and -)	$3 \times 4 + 4 - 0$ $16 \times 2 - 16$
2u x 2u x 2u 4u x 2u x 1u	Volume of 8 units cubed	1u x 2u x 4u 2u x 2u x 2u
6^2 10^2 - 64	36 (Using exponents)	5^2 + 11 4^2 + 4^2 + 2^2

VERSION 2: Either using a paper that the students fold or one that the teacher has printed out (best for younger students who might need guidance with spacing), students work individually on a whiteboard to find a solution. When one student has found a solution for the first number, the student will write their equations on their side and fold the paper so the other student can't see. The second student will do the same when they are finished, which will continue until all equations are written.

When all equations have been written, the students will then uncover their solutions. The students can then compare, check equations, and ask questions. Some questions might include: Why did you choose to use parentheses? Can you explain how you arrived at this answer?

VERSION 3: Digital Option: Students begin much the same way as they would with paper and pencil. However, when they type their responses each student will place a solid shape over their response

Lisa

No matter which option you choose, students will need to think critically about their work as well as the work of their peers. It may be a struggle for some students to accept feedback, but they will become more comfortable giving and receiving with practice.

to keep it hidden until the end. After all equations have been written, students can uncover to compare, check, and ask questions.

VERSION 4: White Board Only Option: Give each student one number and parameters written on the board for all to see. Individually, students work on the equations. When both students are ready, they show their equations to their partner to compare, check, and ask questions.

Adaptations for Primary Students:

For younger students, use a Draw-Pair-Share format, which works in much the same way, but with drawings. If students are working on adding, the students may want to draw different shapes with the addition sign between the pictures. For example, if the teacher gives the number 5, students might draw 😄 😄 😄 + 🖤 🖤 to represent $3 + 2 = 5$.

Pro Tip: Use a fishbowl method to teach your class how to do this protocol: Two students, or the teacher and two students working together, model for the class. The teacher should model how to check the other student's equation and question, then allow the two students to work together to check and ask a question.

If you choose the digital version of this EduProtocol, the shape used for covering the work must be added after text boxes are added, or it will remain under the work that needs to be covered.

Chapter 20
Stacking and Smashing

Gravity is the only "glue" that holds these structures in equilibrium.

—Michael Grab, stone balancing artist

The Art of Stacking

We have learned how to use a protocol for classroom instruction to reduce the cognitive load on students and allow them to refocus on the content instead of the task. But what happens when the content becomes more complicated or longer than one EduProtocol can handle?

One way to organize classroom instruction that is too lengthy for one EduProtocol is to stack one EduProtocol on top of another, like rocks balanced in a tower, to allow students to tackle a longer or more complicated stretch of the curriculum in segments.

Jon

Rocks stacked like this are called "trail ducks." Duck: to go first or lead the way. Another name for them is "cairns." Cairn | a landmark. (Sorry. My teacher brain couldn't help pointing this out.)

Stacks may be completed within one period, or they may take more than one day. Keep pacing in mind as students work through the stack—just the right amount of time for the right amount of content!

Let the Stacking Begin!

Using an old favorite, Cyber Sandwich, let's take a look at how the stacking process works.

Background: Cyber Sandwich is an EduProtocol in which students read a word problem or other math-related content using the annotation methods taught and practiced in their particular classroom while also taking bullet-point notes. Students then work with a partner to Venn diagram the bullet points, looking for key factors in understanding and setting up the math problem or math-related content. Then, using new knowledge and insights gleaned from the discussion, each student writes their summarizing paragraph on how to set up the problem, their comprehension of the math-related content, or the set-up of a math problem.

To use the stacking concept with Cyber Sandwich, find a math problem that is long enough to be broken up and can sustain students through two or more cycles of moving from one part to the next. Alternatively, you can use two or more related passages that build on a topic or concept. Students will complete two or more Cyber Sandwiches in a row.

Use a timer to keep everyone on track. There are times when students work best at their own pace, but the Cyber Sandwich EduProtocol is designed to keep a group or class moving along at the same pace.

Smashing

Some EduProtocols are naturally more suitable for stacking; others are more suitable for smashing! Just as a monster truck can take on a row of cars by approaching one at a time, we can move through the curriculum by proceeding through one protocol at a time.

In Convince Me That, students convince other students of the correct answer in a lively whole-class setting. In Cyber Sandwich, students dive deep into setting up and solving a problem with a partner, and in Comic Strip Math, students set up and explain a problem on their own—perhaps even as an assessment. These three EduProtocols smashed into a sequence sets up a natural gradual release of responsibility as students solve math problems.

Directions for the Cyber Sandwich EduProtocol are on page 8.

English Language Learner Tip: *Learning a new language is hard work. Allow students the gift of familiarity that the EduProtocols provide and scaffold in strong ELL strategies such as intentional partner groups, pre-teaching vocabulary, curriculum walkthroughs, and sentence starters.*

Jon

Teach students to finish by curating five Cyber Sandwiches into a five-paragraph report!

Marlena

We do that by providing just the right amount of content for the right amount of time!

Marlena

I like to think of Smashing like a Pac-Man game, crunching our way through the content.

Marlena

Form follows function, so how many times each EduProtocol repeats in a smash should be dictated by the content covered.

Jon

Nothing spells panic like too much too fast. Kids will shut down and reject the EduProtocol rollout. Keep it light and quick with low chances of failure.

All you need are two EduProtocols to begin smashing.

EduProtocol Smashing is the process of moving through the curriculum by mixing two or more EduProtocols in a series in order to accommodate more complicated or more protracted curriculum tasks in a series of lessons that come together to form a progression.

Getting started with EduProtocol Smashing is easy! Simply master a minimum of any two EduProtocols individually, then combine them into one smash.

Two or more protocols in any order can create an effective smash.

As you and your students master a new protocol, you may decide to add it to the mix. Be cautious about complicating an already complicated process by adding brand new protocols into the row. Too much too fast would defeat the purpose of the EduProtocols by raising the students' affective filter.

We want EduProtocols to slow the technology curve in order to speed up the curriculum learning curve. Adding brand-new protocols to the smash has the potential to defeat this essential purpose.

Call to Action

Choose an EduProtocol you have used in the past with your students and try stacking or smashing with some of your content. Adjust the EduProtocol as needed as you strive to find the right assignment length for the attention span of your students. Reflect on how it worked and make notes for next time.

Many of the EduProtocols are built to stack or smash! As students get faster, the master teacher will add technical details and skills to increase the cognitive load and deepen rigor for students *instead* of switching to a new activity. The EduProtocol then becomes the tool, not the main focus.

Reflect on the process. How did you do with the new combination? How did your students do? What might you need to adjust for next time? Repeat this exact stack/smash with new content to allow your students time to become more familiar with this new process before trying a new combination.

Jon

We have to lose some time in the beginning to gain time in the end. It is not an "if" but a "when." However, by artfully developing high-tempo, low-fail activities we can make the "lost" time just the bare minimum, literally two to three reps. The payoff is having kids who are agile, comfortable, and capable the rest of the year. Priceless.

Chapter 21
No Time Like the Present

It's the job that's never started as takes longest to finish.

—J. R. R. Tolkien, *The Lord of the Rings*

We now know that EduProtocols, like an Instagram post, are tools that can be used again and again with changing content. As students learn the process, they will begin to focus on the "what" of learning instead of on the "how."

We also know this "how" of learning is supported by Dr. Sonny Magana's T3 Framework research. The next step is implementation into your online, blended, or face-to-face classroom.

Start small. Go as slow or as fast as your students can handle the process. You'll know they are ready for the next EduProtocol when they can do the one you have most recently introduced smoothly and without asking, "What do we do next?" again and again. When they know it and can do it with automaticity, then it is time to introduce another one. Remember, not only are they on the learning curve, but you are also! So take it easy.

Follow the directions with fidelity, but adjust as needed. You know your students, how hard to push them, when to back off, and most importantly, how to support their emotional well-being as they study and learn math.

One last piece of implementation advice: Don't automatically back away from the digital format presented in most of these EduProtocols. While paper is best for some, try using circles, squares, numbers, and other items placed on a slide as manipulatives. Consider using audio recording assists such as Screencastify to record directions for students if you cannot walk them through every step, and tools such as Flipgrid to enhance student responses. These options are all great additions to any EduProtocol. Use them consistently and students will eventually be able to use them as tools instead of toys!

Call to Action

Now is your time to get to work. Choose one to three EduProtocols and make a plan for implementation with your content. Tip: spread them out about a month apart, or as needed for a smooth mastery of the process. Now go have fun with your students, and be sure to share your successes with us at @nowatechie, @mathkaveli, @jcorippo, and @mhebern, and at #EduProtocols!

EduProtocols Implementation Planning Guide

EduProtocol			
Date of Lesson Introduction			
Rep 1: Light Content			
Date of Lesson			
Rep 2: Light Content			
Date of Lesson			
Rep 3: Content			
Date of Lesson			
Rep 4: Content			
Date of Lesson			
Rep 5: Full Content			

Acknowledgments

Jeremiah

Thank you to Dave and everyone supporting Dave Burgess Consulting, Inc. for this incredible opportunity. A big thank you to the EduProtocols team, especially Jon and Marlena for being our stewards and shepherding us through this process. Finally, I want to give a huge thanks to Lisa for her inspiration, her humor, her openness, and for letting me be a part of this journey.

Lisa

Thank you to Dave and Shelley Burgess and Dave Burgess Consulting, Inc. for supporting our vision. A huge thank you to Marlena Hebern and Jon Corippo, without whom this journey would not have been possible. I would also like to thank my 2018–19 fifth-grade class for being at the forefront of this book and giving valuable feedback; special thanks goes to Nichole and Xavier for being the leaders in shaping Comic Strip Math. Thank you to Bret Harrison, Tressa Luke, Meghan Cannon-Johann, Kristan Morales, and Kim Voge for not only providing feedback but being early adopters and advocates of MathReps. Thank you to Cris McKee for collaborating and letting me bounce ideas off of you. Finally, a huge thank you to my co-author, Jeremiah, for agreeing to join me on this crazy journey and being such a force in the math and MathReps world. You rock!

We hope that you enjoyed reading this math edition of the *EduProtocol Field Guide* and are putting your new T3 knowledge and math protocols to good use with students. If you would like to go deeper with EduProtocols or the T3 Framework, we recommend reading *The EduProtocol Field Guide, Book 1* and *Book 2* and *Disruptive Classroom Technologies: A Framework for Innovation in Education.*

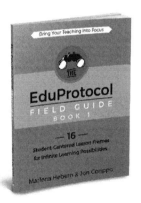

The EduProtocol Field Guide, Book 1, by Marlena Hebern and Jon Corippo

The original sixteen EduProtocols are explained in this book with directions and tips for success. This book also contains the story of Tommy, guidelines for Smart Start, building culture in a classroom, and recalibrating creativity with the Four Cs Throwdown. (Note: The math-specific protocols from this book, Learning in the Round, and 3-Act Math® were reprinted in *The EduProtocol Field Guide: Math Edition*.)

The EduProtocol Field Guide, Book 2, by Marlena Hebern and Jon Corippo

An additional twelve EduProtocols are included in *The EduProtocol Field Guide, Book 2*, along with remixes inspired by readers using some of the original sixteen EduProtocols. Book 2 also contains insights into how instructional design theories underpin the protocols, stacking and smashing EduProtocols, and how the EduProtocols fit into the Universal Design for Learning classroom.

Notes

Chapter 4

1. Sonny Magana, *Disruptive Classroom Technologies* (New York: Oxford University Research Encyclopedia of Education, 2019), PDF, https://s23.a2zinc.net/clients/cosn/cosn2020/Custom/Handout/Speaker8_Session32_1.pdf.

2. Sonny Magana and Robert Marzano, *Enhancing the Art and Science of Teaching with Technology* (Bloomington, IN: Solution Tree Press, 2014).

3. Sonny Magana, "Enhancing the Art and Science of Teaching with Technology: A Model for Improving Learning for All Students," (doctoral dissertation, Seattle University, 2016).

4. Sonny Magana, *Disruptive Classroom Technologies: A Framework for Innovation in Education,* (Thousand Oaks, CA: Corwin Press, 2017).

5. Sonny Magana, *Disrupting Low-Impact Technology Use: Aligning Visible Learning and the T3 Framework for Innovation* (Thousand Oaks, CA: Corwin Press, 2019), PDF, https://maganaeducation.com/wp-content/uploads/2019/06/Magana_Disrupting-Low-Impact-Technology-Use_FINAL.pdf.

6. Sonny Magana, *The 7 Habits of Meta-Learners,* (Redmond, WA: Magana Education Press, forthcoming).

Chapter 7

1. Sian Beilock, "Back to School: Dealing with Academic Stress," *Psychological Science Agenda Newsletter,* American Psychological Association, September 2011, https://www.apa.org/science/about/psa/2011/09/academic-stress.

2. Jo Boaler, "Timed Tests and the Development of Math Anxiety," *Stanford Graduate School of Education,* 3 July 2012, https://ed.stanford.edu/news/boaler-timed-tests-and-development-math-anxiety.

3. Gerardo Ramirez et al. "Math Anxiety, Working Memory, and Math Achievement in Early Elementary School," *Journal of Cognition and*

Development 14, no. 2 (2013), https://doi.org/10.1080/15248372.2012
.664593.

4. Marlena Hebern and Jon Corippo, *The EduProtocol Field Guide, Book 1: 16 Student-Centered Lesson Frames for Infinite Learning Possibilities* (San Diego, CA: Dave Burgess Consulting, Inc., 2018).

Chapter 9

1. Sian L. Beilock and Daniel T. Willingham, "Math Anxiety: Can Teachers Help Students Reduce It?" *American Education* (Summer 2014), https://www.aft.org/sites/default/files/periodicals/beilock.pdf.

2. Marlena Hebern and Jon Corippo, *The EduProtocol Field Guide, Book 1: 16 Student-Centered Lesson Frames for Infinite Learning Possibilities* (San Diego, CA: Dave Burgess Consulting, Inc., 2018), 170.

Chapter 10

1. Marlena Hebern and Jon Corippo, *The EduProtocol Field Guide, Book 1: 16 Student-Centered Lesson Frames for Infinite Learning Possibilities* (San Diego, CA: Dave Burgess Consulting, Inc., 2018), 173–4.

Chapter 14

1. Robert J. Marzano and Debra J. Pickering, *Building Academic Vocabulary* (Alexandria, VA: ASCD Publications, 2005), 64.

Chapter 15

1. LeAnn Garrett, "Dewey, Dale, and Bruner: Educational Philosophy, Experiential Learning, and Library School Cataloging Instruction," *Journal of Education for Library and Information Science* 38, no. 2 (Spring 1997), https://eric.ed.gov/?id=EJ573992.

Chapter 17

1. This EduProtocol was inspired by Number Talks, created by Kathy Richardson and Ruth Parker in the early 1990s. Number talks with images + equations + word problems = Write Bytes.

Chapter 18

1. Andrei Scheinkman, "The 52 Best—And Weirdest—Charts We Made In 2016," *FiveThirtyEight*, 30 December 2016, fivethirtyeight.com/features/the-52-best-and-weirdest-charts-we-made-in-2016.

Image Credits

Chapter 6

Frayer: Meghan Cannon-Johann @JohannMundy

Geometry MathRep: Kristan Morales

Chapter 11

Photo Credit: Ed Campos

Chapter 13

Depth of Knowledge in Mathematics Chart created and used with permission by Sean Junkins

Chapter 15

Image credit: Christine Pinto and Jessica Twomey

Chapter 17

Donut illustrations by siberian beard from Pixabay

About the Authors

Lisa Nowakowski is a twenty-six-year veteran teacher known for her energy and strong connections with students. She has been able to bring her passion for student engagement, technology integration, and hands-on learning to both teachers and students in fun and easily accessible methods.

Growing up in the Detroit area, Lisa has a healthy appreciation of sports. She worked alongside her father and grandfather at the family butcher shop. This is where she grew a healthy appreciation of math. Let's just say that the cash register was so old, it only accepted the sale amount, and her grandpa Zig would only allow mental math when calculating change for customers. Ask her about those times; she has many fun stories that will keep you entertained for hours.

Lisa began her teaching career in Michigan before moving to the Salinas Valley on California's Central Coast. Throughout her career, she has taught various grades at the elementary level. She has experience with everything from kinder to fifth grade. As a district technology leader, she pioneered 1:1 Chromebooks in her district. Most recently, she accepted a Tech TOSA position in her district in order to make a greater impact on the students and educators in her community.

Lisa is an accomplished educator. She is a Google Innovator and Trainer. She belongs to CUE (a California-based non-profit organization dedicated to bringing tech integration into districts) where she is a Lead Learner. Lisa holds a Master's in Education that focused on diverse learners. She also has a podcast with Nancy Minicozzi (@coffeenancy) called T.L.C. (Tech. Learn. Coffee.) that can be heard on the first and third Monday of every month. And of course, she's the creator and curator of MathReps.

Lisa enjoys the small farming community in which she lives. Where she appreciates the close-knit community and the friendships it brings. As a runner–a slow and grumbly one–she often runs 5K and 10K races with Team Sloth (a close group of friends of all ages). She shares her home with her two adorable puppers. A day doesn't go by where she doesn't talk with her dad.

Jeremiah Ruesch is a consultant for the Kings County Office of Education. Prior to serving the districts of Kings County, Jeremiah worked for six years as the math coordinator and instructional coach for a K–12 district. Jeremiah is passionate about fostering curiosity and promoting a growth mindset in mathematics for all learners. Before teaching high school in 2008, Jeremiah taught mathematics at the college level. Since 2013, Jeremiah has been uncovering the mathematical understanding of learners of all ages, incorporating technology as a tool for learners to access and enhance their learning. Jeremiah firmly believes in the power of being a connected educator, investing in others, and growing better together. Jeremiah spends his spare time chasing after his toddler, or recovering from chasing after his toddler, while his patient wife has to put up with both boys.

For over thirty years, **Marlena Hebern** has been a passionate educator, putting her heart and soul into her work and loving every minute. Marlena is driven by kids and her desire to make learning fun and engaging for all students. Through her career as teacher, coach, administrator, and technology integration specialist, she has learned the value of relationships and supporting teachers.

Marlena Hebern's gentle and calm approach connects well with educators, especially those struggling to keep up. She draws upon her eighteen years of classroom experience, expertise with the EduProtocols, and Cognitive Coaching training to inspire and excite teachers about the possibilities of great instruction!

Marlena's early passion for education began with her tenure as a Girl Scout camp counselor in college. She realized early on that school should be like camp: hands on learning, fun projects, emphasis on social entrepreneurship, lasting friendships, independence, and student voice.

Marlena Hebern and her co-author were honored in 2020 as the recipients of the EdTech Awards in the category of Leader Setting a Trend. Marlena has also been recognized as a Beginning Teacher Support Provider of the Year and has a master's degree in Reading Instruction. She is also a Google Certified Innovator and a Google Certified Trainer. Marlena also presents at local and regional conferences including CUE and ISTE.

Marlena enjoys her rural home near Yosemite National Park and the outdoors with her husband, who is a talented (and retired) multimedia/video teacher. They are very proud of their two daughters, who are now starting their own families and embarking on their young careers in engineering and geography.

Jon Corippo describes himself as a "formerly disgruntled student." He made it almost all the way through school at a 2.9 GPA. His final three semesters in advertising changed everything, though: advertising classes were project based. Jon's grades shot to nearly 4.0. Also while at Fresno State, Jon served as a graduate assistant football coach, learning about leadership and teaching at the feet of Jim Sweeney. Jon graduated college with no intention of teaching.

After about seven years in non-educational jobs, Jon's amazing wife persuaded him to try his hand in education: he was hooked after just two days as a long-term sub on an emergency credential.

About twenty years later, Jon had served a decade at the K–8 level, opened a 1-1, PBL, Google-based high school, served in two county offices, including as an Assistant Superintendent and IT Director. Jon has been recognized a County Teacher of the Year, a 20 to Watch Educator by the NSBA, a 100 to Watch Educator, and was a finalist and a winner in the EdTech Digest Awards for Eduprotocols. Jon also holds the Apple Distinguished Educator, Google Certified Innovator, and Microsoft Innovative Educator badges.

Jon is very proud of his work with CUE, where he served as the Chief Learning Officer. His work with CUE included creating the CUE Rock Star concept of Professional Development, with a focus on hands-on learning and getting teachers connected via social media. Jon led the development of the very successful CUE Google Launch program and the well received CUE BOLD Symposium. Under Jon's leadership, CUE professional learning trained over 50,000 educators.

Jon is currently teaching sixth grade in Madera at Hillside School, researching a new teaching book, and making new EduProtocols.

Jon lives in Coarsegold, California, near Yosemite, with his wife (a very successful educator), three children, and a random number of free-range chickens.

More from

Since 2012, DBCI has been publishing books that inspire and equip educators to be their best. For more information on our titles or to purchase bulk orders for your school, district, or book study, visit **DaveBurgessConsulting.com/DBCIbooks**.

More Teaching Methods & Materials

All 4s and 5s by Andrew Sharos
Boredom Busters by Katie Powell
The Classroom Chef by John Stevens and Matt Vaudrey
The Collaborative Classroom by Trevor Muir
Copyrighteous by Diana Gill
CREATE by Bethany J. Petty
Ditch That Homework by Matt Miller and Alice Keeler
Ditch That Textbook by Matt Miller
Don't Ditch That Tech by Matt Miller, Nate Ridgway, and Angelia Ridgway
EDrenaline Rush by John Meehan
Educated by Design by Michael Cohen, The Tech Rabbi
The EduProtocol Field Guide by Marlena Hebern and Jon Corippo
The EduProtocol Field Guide: Book 2 by Marlena Hebern and Jon Corippo
Game On? Brain On! by Lindsay Portnoy, PhD
Innovating Play by Jessica LaBar-Twomy and Christine Pinto
Instant Relevance by Denis Sheeran
LAUNCH by John Spencer and A.J. Juliani
Make Learning MAGICAL by Tisha Richmond
Pass the Baton by Kathryn Finch and Theresa Hoover
Project-Based Learning Anywhere by Lori Elliott
Pure Genius by Don Wettrick
The Revolution by Darren Ellwein and Derek McCoy
Shift This! by Joy Kirr
Skyrocket Your Teacher Coaching by Michael Cary Sonbert
Spark Learning by Ramsey Musallam
Sparks in the Dark by Travis Crowder and Todd Nesloney
Table Talk Math by John Stevens
Unpack Your Impact by Naomi O'Brien and LaNesha Tabb
The Wild Card by Hope and Wade King
The Writing on the Classroom Wall by Steve Wyborney

Like a PIRATE™ Series

Teach Like a PIRATE by Dave Burgess
eXPlore Like a PIRATE by Michael Matera
Learn Like a PIRATE by Paul Solarz
Play Like a PIRATE by Quinn Rollins
Run Like a PIRATE by Adam Welcome
Tech Like a PIRATE by Matt Miller

Lead Like a PIRATE™ Series

Lead Like a PIRATE by Shelley Burgess and Beth Houf
Balance Like a PIRATE by Jessica Cabeen, Jessica Johnson, and Sarah Johnson
Lead beyond Your Title by Nili Bartley
Lead with Appreciation by Amber Teamann and Melinda Miller
Lead with Culture by Jay Billy
Lead with Instructional Rounds by Vicki Wilson
Lead with Literacy by Mandy Ellis

Leadership & School Culture

Culturize by Jimmy Casas
Escaping the School Leader's Dunk Tank by Rebecca Coda and Rick Jetter
Fight Song by Kim Bearden
From Teacher to Leader by Starr Sackstein
If the Dance Floor Is Empty, Change the Song by Joe Clark
The Innovator's Mindset by George Couros
It's OK to Say "They" by Christy Whittlesey
Kids Deserve It! by Todd Nesloney and Adam Welcome
Let Them Speak by Rebecca Coda and Rick Jetter
The Limitless School by Abe Hege and Adam Dovico
Live Your Excellence by Jimmy Casas
Next-Level Teaching by Jonathan Alsheimer
The Pepper Effect by Sean Gaillard
Principaled by Kate Barker, Kourtney Ferrua, and Rachael George
The Principled Principal by Jeffrey Zoul and Anthony McConnell
Relentless by Hamish Brewer
The Secret Solution by Todd Whitaker, Sam Miller, and Ryan Donlan
Start. Right. Now. by Todd Whitaker, Jeffrey Zoul, and Jimmy Casas
Stop. Right. Now. by Jimmy Casas and Jeffrey Zoul
Teachers Deserve It by Rae Hughart and Adam Welcome

Teach Your Class Off by CJ Reynolds
They Call Me "Mr. De" by Frank DeAngelis
Thrive through the Five by Jill M. Siler
Unmapped Potential by Julie Hasson and Missy Lennard
When Kids Lead by Todd Nesloney and Adam Dovico
Word Shift by Joy Kirr
Your School Rocks by Ryan McLane and Eric Lowe

Technology & Tools

50 Things You Can Do with Google Classroom by Alice Keeler and Libbi Miller
50 Things to Go Further with Google Classroom by Alice Keeler and Libbi Miller
140 Twitter Tips for Educators by Brad Currie, Billy Krakower, and Scott Rocco
Block Breaker by Brian Aspinall
Building Blocks for Tiny Techies by Jamila "Mia" Leonard
Code Breaker by Brian Aspinall
The Complete EdTech Coach by Katherine Goyette and Adam Juarez
Control Alt Achieve by Eric Curts
The Esports Education Playbook by Chris Aviles, Steve Isaacs, Christine Lion-Bailey, and Jesse Lubinsky
Google Apps for Littles by Christine Pinto and Alice Keeler
Master the Media by Julie Smith
Reality Bytes by Christine Lion-Bailey, Jesse Lubinsky, and Micah Shippee, PhD
Sail the 7 Cs with Microsoft Education by Becky Keene and Kathi Kersznowski
Shake Up Learning by Kasey Bell
Social LEADia by Jennifer Casa-Todd
Stepping up to Google Classroom by Alice Keeler and Kimberly Mattina
Teaching Math with Google Apps by Alice Keeler and Diana Herrington
Teachingland by Amanda Fox and Mary Ellen Weeks

Inspiration, Professional Growth & Personal Development

Be REAL by Tara Martin
Be the One for Kids by Ryan Sheehy
The Coach ADVenture by Amy Illingworth
Creatively Productive by Lisa Johnson
Educational Eye Exam by Alicia Ray
The EduNinja Mindset by Jennifer Burdis
Empower Our Girls by Lynmara Colón and Adam Welcome
Finding Lifelines by Andrew Grieve and Andrew Sharos
The Four O'Clock Faculty by Rich Czyz
How Much Water Do We Have? by Pete and Kris Nunweiler

P Is for Pirate by Dave and Shelley Burgess
A Passion for Kindness by Tamara Letter
The Path to Serendipity by Allyson Apsey
Sanctuaries by Dan Tricarico
Saving Sycamore by Molly B. Hudgens
The SECRET SAUCE by Rich Czyz
Shattering the Perfect Teacher Myth by Aaron Hogan
Stories from Webb by Todd Nesloney
Talk to Me by Kim Bearden
Teach Better by Chad Ostrowski, Tiffany Ott, Rae Hughart, and Jeff Gargas
Teach Me, Teacher by Jacob Chastain
Teach, Play, Learn! by Adam Peterson
The Teachers of Oz by Herbie Raad and Nathan Lang-Raad
TeamMakers by Laura Robb and Evan Robb
Through the Lens of Serendipity by Allyson Apsey
The Zen Teacher by Dan Tricarico

Children's Books

Beyond Us by Aaron Polansky
Cannonball In by Tara Martin
Dolphins in Trees by Aaron Polansky
I Want to Be a Lot by Ashley Savage
The Princes of Serendip by Allyson Apsey
Ride with Emilio by Richard Nares
The Wild Card Kids by Hope and Wade King
Zom-Be a Design Thinker by Amanda Fox

Made in the USA
Las Vegas, NV
04 April 2024

88242904R00083